Tammy!

Hey girl, he[y] ... way from meeting in J's apartment! Thank you for your friendship over the years. I am so proud of you for all you are doing and have overcome.

GOD'S GOT JOKES

Keep kickin' ass and inspiring us along the way!

Miracles + Blessings,

Nee Ro 3/2022

P.S. I hope to see you soon!!

GOD'S GOT JOKES

HOW I USED MY FAITH AND GOD'S HUMOR TO SURVIVE BREAST CANCER

NEOSHO C. PONDER, PHD

NEW DEGREE PRESS

GOD'S GOT JOKES

How I Used My Faith and God's Humor to Survive Breast Cancer

ISBN   978-1-63730-816-5   *Paperback*

978-1-63730-878-3   *Kindle Ebook*

978-1-63730-972-8   *Ebook*

For my father Gene, brother Victor, and friend Brandon who started this journey with me on earth and then decided to get a better view.

To all the survivors, especially my brother, Vincent. The more you laugh the better you will feel. Try it. I dare you!

CONTENTS

AUTHOR'S NOTE

———

Coming to the stage...the Original King of Comedy ... G ... O ... D!!

God is the original king of comedy (no shade to Uncle Steve and 'nem) and after reading this book about my breast cancer journey, you will understand why I feel this way. From ironic timing to bad professional decisions to personal losses, I refused to see that God is laughing at all of my plans and guiding me to where He wants me to be. It took a complete breakdown and a whole ass conversation with God about my purpose for me to start laughing at my messed-up situation.

And then, I discovered Clarence, a 2.8 cm tumor in my left breast.

After earning my doctorate, I was expected to be a thought leader, someone who would be sought-after for my opinion on deep discourse, which would lead to requests to speak at conferences, sit on panels, and contribute published works. The expectations people had of me were daunting, but I was excited and nervous about what was next for me. I believed my doctoral degree would guarantee me a comfortable life. I let people's expectation of me define me and order my steps when I should have looked to God for guidance.

As a Black woman, you are always looked at as strong, and then to be an educated Black woman you are expected to have your stuff together. Everyone assumed that because I had a PhD, I would have no problems getting a job, earning a comfortable salary, and having the emotional capacity to sustain an intimate relationship. Then, on Friday, April 8, 2016, at 5:37 p.m., almost a year to the date of my dissertation defense, I discovered Clarence. It was in this moment that God said, "This is why you can't find a job. I have a bigger job for you."

When I was diagnosed with breast cancer, I put on my "I'm ready to fight" face. Instead of wallowing in self-pity, I took on my assignment like a champ: a broke, unemployed, emotional mess of a champ. That was, as they say in comedic writing, the premise of God's joke.

In so many actions, God was saying, "Girl, you are not all that!" Maybe I knew that I wasn't all that, but I was afraid of others knowing that fact.

Historically, in the Black community, we don't talk about what we're going through. We're not transparent about our health: mental, physical, or financial. I was more afraid of telling the world about my cancer than of the disease itself. I struggled with the dichotomy between being silent about my mental and physical health and sharing for fear of not getting hired in certain spaces. I did not want to be seen as a liability for future employment or a burden to friends and family. I was so used to being healthy and taking care of others that I didn't know how to just *be*.

So, I shared my diagnosis publicly with ebbs and flows of support. But cancer peeled back the mask I'd been donning my entire life. I was always a believer and servant, but I did not have an intimate relationship with God until I met

Clarence. Discovering that ping pong ball in my left breast was God's will. In all of the difficult days, weeks, months, and years, God knew it would allow me to develop a more constant relationship with Him.

As you will see throughout this memoir, God's humor persisted through most of my cancer journey. From homelessness to living in my own place with no full-time job, He shows up and shows out! When I look at my home now, I laugh a little because God has brought me so far. I am unemployed, but not really worried. My faith has provided when I could not. Every time I think I won't make rent or something won't get paid, He makes a way. It is so astounding that I have to laugh!

Early on in my journey, I began to recite the mantra, "faith and prayer do not go with fear and worry." I practiced faith and prayer over fear and worry throughout each battle because I knew that was exactly what I needed to win the war. This practice allowed me to see all the hilarious things that happen to us that we can't explain. I laughed until I cried, but I also prayed and did not lose my faith. (Though I won't lie; it wavered a little.)

After fully processing it, I felt empowered by my prognosis. I refused to look like my situation. I lost my boobs, but because of my faith, I knew I would get new ones. The humor in that is I didn't know all I would have to go through to get the new ones. I lost my hair and prayed for it to come back and it did, but not how I thought. The joke is that India, my hair, acted brand new by growing back a completely different texture for about two and a half years and then voila, the original texture roared back with a vengeance (sans my edges, but I digressed).

You can worry and be afraid of all of these things, or you can laugh and ask, "Really? Really, God?"

He'll respond, "Yes, really. Now, learn from it. Laugh at it. And keep fighting/going."

This book is for everyone, but I believe this book will bless your spirit if you are sitting in the chemo chair and need something to take your mind off the poison being pumped into your body. If you are waiting in the car because you cannot be in the infusion room with a loved one, then you could pass the time by laughing at God's jokes that I endured. If you are a survivor, thriver, or even a denier, this book should inspire, motivate, and force you to face your truth. If you have ever felt like life has kicked you in your ass, then this is your book!

This book is also for those of us who struggle with our relationship with God. You know, us Christians who love Jesus, but cuss a little. Yep, us! This book includes humorous conversations with God with a little commentary from His son, Jesus, and the Holy Spirit. Yes, chile, they team up on me! We all fall short of God's grace, but it is the get-up-and-dust-it-off that is proof of His mercy. My grace and mercy came in the form of a dark humor comedy show which resulted in some difficult lessons, and yours probably does too!

This book is just one perspective of how to handle a life-changing experience such as a cancer diagnosis. This is not "make it make sense" type of news. There are nuggets, anecdotes, awkward giggle moments, and aha chuckles that can save you, or someone you love, the time and energy of trying to *make it make sense.* I found a *mess*age in my mess, *testi*monies in my tests, and humor through my pain. So, be ready for what I understood as God's jokes and take notes;

it's going to be one heck of a ride. I wouldn't want you to miss a thing!

While you read my memoir, please scan the QR code at the end of each chapter. You will find the music that inspired me and illustrated my journey, as well as exclusive photos. This is just for you, my readers! Miracles and blessings.

CHAPTER 1

BECOMING PhinisheD

After spending nearly my entire life in school, I was ready to be Neosho C. Ponder (COMMA) PhD. I was finally PhinisheD (PhD)!

If I could title my last year of school, it would be called *What the Heck Am I Doing*? I learned so much about myself in the final year of my doctoral journey. The summer of 2014, my younger sister, Tianna, got married. This prompted me to figure out how I would go to New Orleans (NOLA) for Essence Festival to see Prince in concert, fulfill my maid of honor duties, and see The Carters' On The Run Tour. Yes, I was doing *the* most! I decided to drive to Kansas City from DC a week before the wedding so I could go to Essence Fest with my girlfriends from high school. After experiencing the greatness of his Purple Majesty, Prince, I headed back to KC to get my sister down the aisle, then went home to DC re-pack and fly *back* to NOLA for the concert. Like I said, *the most*!

This was a whirlwind of a summer, and it put a strain on my finances since I was living off of credit cards. It was also during this time that I had learned that my fellowship would not be renewed after three years. My advisor found me a better one with my own office! That office would be pivotal in completing my dissertation. God definitely comes right on time!

Once back in DC, I had to prepare myself mentally for this final stretch. But just when I was getting my mind right, I learned I had depleted all my federal student loans. *Really, God? Really?* I quickly learned that my sorority had an endowment at the school that would cover the amount I was missing. Although my fellowship covered tuition and gave me a stipend, it wasn't enough to cover living expenses. The loans and now the Delta Scholarship covered my other living expenses. Sheesh... I wasn't sure it could get crazier, but God said, "Oh really? Watch me work!"

In October 2014, I was reading the November edition of *O Magazine.* I had already been struggling with writing my dissertation and reading a magazine was a welcome distraction. There was an article written about women living with adult Attention Deficit Hyperactivity Disorder (ADHD) (Maltby, 2014). An *aha* moment for me was when I had done the research for my dissertation, but could not sit for extended periods of time and write. I asked my primary care physician (PCP) if there was anything I could do to help me focus. I was honestly worried that my physical health was affecting my ability to write my dissertation. He recognized similar traits his wife had when she was struggling to write her dissertation. He prescribed me a low dosage of Adderall, which led to me finishing my entire dissertation in three months!

I submitted the final draft of my dissertation on Wednesday, March 4, 2015. I was preparing for a trip to Selma, Alabama for the 50th Anniversary of Bloody Sunday, March 7, 1965. I used this trip as a deadline for submitting the full

draft of my dissertation to my advisor. In addition to com-
memorating a historic event, I was celebrating my thirty-fifth
birthday on March 9. After writing almost non-stop for three
months, the gravity of this accomplishment hit me after leaving the final draft in my advisor's mailbox and sitting in my
car at the mall. I didn't feel sick, but like air had been released
from me. I burst into a full-on ugly cry right there in the
parking garage of Pentagon City Mall. It was a like a hard
rain: a lot of water in a short amount of time. You know when
you have some good news and just wanna scream it from
the rooftops? That is what it felt like. Then, in true Neosho
fashion, I was on a plane the next day. I never knew how to
just be in the moment. I was always on to the next thing. I'm
sure God was like, "Oh, you gon' learn. Enjoy yourself now
'cause your slowdown is coming."

While in Selma, I witnessed history. President Obama,
Congressman John Lewis, Dr. King's children, and other
living marchers from that historic day marched across the
Edmund Pettus Bridge. The pictures of that day do no justice!
It was hot, humid, and jubilant. The people of Selma were
so warm and welcoming. The day after President Obama's
speech, I walked the bridge and snapped so many pictures.
I am still in awe to this day of how impactful that weekend
in Selma was. I cherish those memories and am so blessed
to have had opportunity to pay homage to those who fought
and died for my right to vote. This was just the motivation I
needed to cross the finish line of finishing school.

I defended my dissertation, Monday, April 20, 2015, and
was approved with little revisions. The following weekend, I
attended my college BFF, Anthony's, wedding in Milwaukee,
where I first met my sista-friend, Monica. Then, I spent a few
days in Chicago to decompress from school. I left Chicago on

April 29 and flew to Kansas City (KC) to surprise my sister, Tianna for her thirty-fourth birthday, then headed back to Washington, DC (DC) to prepare for graduation. Yes, I did all of this because I love being there for those that I love, but it was time to focus on graduation.

Since they both had health issues during my time in graduate school, I prayed my biological father, Gene, and brother, Victor, could make the trip from KC to DC. Gene had attended only one graduation of mine: high school. Since this was my last one, I was glad they made the trip. I later realized that you have to be careful what you pray for. Thankfully, they made it and all went well, but I wished I would have prayed for them to make it to more milestones in my life. God is very specific therefore, we must be specific about our prayers.

After graduation, armed with my doctorate and a network of amazingly successful friends, I was ready to take on the world. While interviewing for jobs, I was offered an adjunct teaching position at Trinity Washington University. Dr. Patricia Love, a Howard Alum, saw me on campus and asked if I was working. When I shared that I was looking, she asked if I would be willing to teach communications classes part-time until I found something.

Patricia was a feisty, no-nonsense woman who had a full career before beginning her doctorate at Howard, so she was quite seasoned. When I learned we were sorority sisters (sorors), it made sense. Those types of accomplishments were common amongst our sorors. I did not know she was Black until I heard her voice. She is fair-skinned with short, curly, salt-and-pepper hair, but it's not kinky. There is something about the voice and tone of a Black woman where you just know. I was excited to work with her in this newly created program where I could teach while looking for a job. What I later realized was that Patricia offered me a gift. Trinity was my saving grace during my cancer journey. I had a teaching job during treatment, after surgeries, and while struggling to find full-time employment.

I remained steadfast in my pursuit of a full-time job, but began to wonder if what I wanted to do matched the person people saw when I showed up for interviews. I did not know what masking was at the time, but now I know my ADHD could have been somewhat of a hinderance. I had been masking professionally and by the end of that summer, I began to see it had caught up with me and was spilling over into my dating life.

Four months after finishing school, I met Desmond at a Congressional Black Caucus event. We hit it off instantly! We spent the next five months getting acquainted. Then after a difficult job search, I began to lose confidence and drive, which caused Desmond to step back. He said he wanted me to get myself together, which, due to my insecurity, translated into, "you're not good enough, ambitious enough, or confident enough to be with me." I sought help from a therapist, but as soon as I began seeing her, I discovered Clarence.

When 2015 ended, I figured things could only get better in 2016. What was supposed to be the most successful year of my life became the most embarrassing, so I decided to stay in DC for the 2015 holidays. In ten years of living out-of-town, I had never missed Christmas in Kansas City. It was meant to be an adult decision. I figured I'd use that time to enjoy Christmas Day service at my church and dinner with my landlord and her son. While those were great times, I still felt alone at Christmas. In those moments of loneliness, I knew the real reason I missed Christmas with my family was because I was embarrassed. I was the most educated person on either sides of my family and yet, I did not have a job.

Instead of praying and fasting, I suffered in silence and kept declining possible opportunities that could have led to a full-time position. *How Sway? Where they do that at?* And to top it all off, I was invited for two final interviews for different positions at the same organization only to not get either position. I cannot believe I did not take more advantage of *every* opportunity. I now know I had a humility issue!

I have thought about that final year of normalcy a lot since being diagnosed with adult ADHD. I definitely sung my "shoulda, coulda, wouldas," but it brought on depression and anxiety. It was in those moments when I looked to my faith and trusted that He would see me through. In a lot of ways, I believe the year preceding my cancer diagnosis was preparing me for the tears, pain, and lessons that were to come.

What was I becoming? Was I truly PhinisheD? I had so much to learn! I was schoolin' life, as Bey would say, and God, Jesus, and the Holy Spirit were my professors. While at times I feel like I am in a Key and Peele skit, class is always in session.

CHAPTER 2

#TOUCHYOURBOOBS

———

On Friday, April 8, 2016, I adjusted my left breast inside of a tank top and felt a lump. My heart sank. I looked at the clock. It was at 5:37 p.m. ET. I knew my life would never be the same.

I was an adjunct professor, so Monday through Wednesday I spent several hours a day in my office meeting and working with students and then held class on most Thursday evenings. Fridays were my rest days. I usually lay in bed most of the day and catch up on my DVR. So, on this particular day, I was exhausted. While lying in bed, thinking about my upcoming health cleanse, I remembered my soror (sorority sister), and her husband had been on a juice cleanse since January. In addition to getting healthy, they had lost several pounds. I called to pick her brain about my upcoming green smoothie cleanse.

It was great catching up and hearing about their plans to have a baby. As she was asking me about my health plans, I was untwisting my tank top. As I moved my left breast over to the inside of the tank, I gasped and looked at the clock. Amina was still talking and, in my head, I was telling her to hold on, but no sound came out. Then, the sound came.

"Amina... Wait... Hold up," I said breathlessly. It felt like the wind had been knocked out of me. Naturally, I immediately felt the other breast.

"Huh? What?" she responded.

"Girl... I...," I struggled to find the words.

"What... What? You okay?" she exclaimed.

"Amina... I just felt a lump in my boob and I need a minute," I said.

"Girl, what! Oh my God, are you sure?"

"Yes, and I just checked the other side too. It's just the left side. I don't know what to do. I need to see if Rhonda's home. I need someone else to feel this," I said.

"Wait, who is Rhonda? You need to go to the doctor and have it checked." This was great advice that I wasn't ready to hear.

"Rhonda is my landlord and friend. She lives upstairs. Let me see if she is home. Let me let you go."

"Okay, well keep me posted, but I'm sure it will be okay."

"Thank you. Talk to you later."

After I got off the phone, I conducted a *full* self-breast exam, both standing and laying down. Honestly, I didn't know if I was even doing it correctly, but I knew I had felt something that shouldn't be there! *Thank God* I felt nothing abnormal in my right breast. As I began processing that I felt a lump in my breast, I knew my life was changed *forever*!

As I was coming to grips with what was happening, I heard God say, "This is why you couldn't find a job. I have a bigger job for you."

My first course of action was to have someone else touch it just to make sure I wasn't crazy, but Rhonda was not home. Instead of staying home and freaking out, I went about my evening as planned: solo date night. While I remember what

I ate and drank, I cannot remember what movie I saw. It was the last showing of the night. I sat in the theater and I remember talking to God aloud.

I said, "I am not ready. God, I am not ready. There is so much I have not done. I'm not ready."

"Then you have to fight. *You* have to decide and then do it."

"Okay, I will," I replied. So much of that evening was in slow motion.

I don't ever remember having more clarity than I did in that moment. I knew what I had to do. Fight! It was not his words that motivated me, but it was his presence of assuredness that, while low-key, hyped me up. I felt like a boxer in the ring about to be introduced in a title fight, a fight that could make or break my career or, in this case, take my life. It was as if I was Ali, the lump was Frazier, and God was Bundini. Sitting in that dark theater, watching a movie I cannot recall, I made the decision to fight for my life, my career, and my future. *Let's go!*

The next day, I immediately texted my landlord, Rhonda, and asked if I could come up and ask her something. I really wanted her to touch it because she worked in healthcare. She felt what I felt, but said it could be a cyst or some sort of calcification. I totally understood what she was saying, but *I knew my boobs* and I've *never* felt anything before, so I just knew. I had never had a broken bone, a cavity, and was rarely sick with even a cold. When you have been relatively healthy your entire life, you can feel when something is wrong.

About a year prior, I had read articles about an increase in breast cancer diagnoses due to the aluminum in deodorant. I immediately stopped wearing deodorant to bed and used lemon juice as a natural deodorant at night. I learned the aluminum plays a role in clogging pores, preventing toxins in the form of sweat from leaving the body. I always touched my boobs and was familiar with how they felt and looked. So, feeling that lump, which was very pronounced, caused a shift in my outlook on life.

Since I felt the lump on a Friday evening, I waited until Monday to make a doctor's appointment. I went about my life, but saw things through a different lens. I did not want to freak anyone else out, so I still went to campus and met with students like I always had done. It was probably one of the longest two weeks of my life. It was hard not to talk to anyone about it because I am a sharer and sometimes an oversharer. I had never kept something like *this* to myself, but I wanted to make sure I knew what was going on before bringing others into this alternate universe. I still touched the lump throughout the week in hopes that it would go away, but it never did. Thankfully, it didn't grow either. I continued to talk to God.

The week leading up to my doctor's appointment, I felt a shift in my relationship with God. Our conversations began with, "What do you want me to do, Lord? Please, order my steps." Of course, he did not answer in the way I expected and my questions became full on sobs, especially when I touched the lump. "Please take it away, God! Jesus, help me! *Why now*?" I would cry.

There is nothing like the release from a hard cry in the shower. It was in the shower that my conversations with God happened most often. After touching the lump every day and finding it had never left, it became annoying! I began to think of that annoying kid in school that wouldn't go away and the name "Clarence" popped in my mind. I named my tumor because I needed to give it an identity so I would know what I was fighting.

During more than one of our conversations, God told me to fight, but that was it. He said it like a mic drop, as if that was a commandment.

Finally, on Monday, April 18, I saw my new primary care physician, or PCP. My previous PCP moved away the previous year.

"Hello, Ms. Ponder," she said as she quickly entered the room. "I see you are concerned about a lump," she said as she flipped through my chart.

"Yes, ma'am. I found it a couple of weeks ago and it is still there in the same place," I explained.

"Let me see, you're thirty-six... And do you have a family history of breast cancer?" she asked.

"No, ma'am. No history of breast cancer," I said.

"Lay down and let me take a look."

As she was examining me, she explained about cysts and calcifications. I kept reiterating how well I knew my breasts and that the lump was not supposed to be there. I also shared that I'd stopped wearing deodorant to bed, but she seemed so nonchalant. Maybe it was my nerves, but maybe not.

"I just want it scanned or something," I told her.

"Okay, I know you are worried, but you will be surprised how lumpy breasts can be. You have never been told that you have dense breasts before?" she asked.

"No ma'am. I do not have dense breasts. I am very familiar with my breasts, really," I pleaded.

"Okay, Ms. Ponder, I understand. I tell you what..." she said as if she was trying to appease me, "I will order a mammogram, ultrasound, and MRI for you. You have to call and make the appointments, but I will put the orders in. I don't think you have anything to worry about, but let's just make sure. Okay?"

"Okay, so I just have to call and schedule the tests? What number do I call again?" I asked with a sigh of relief.

"They will get you the numbers at the front desk. I am going to go put the orders in now. On your way out, just get that information and we will see, okay?"

As I was gathering my things to go out to the front desk, all I could think was, *why was she so calm about it?* I mean, she had zero sense of urgency. I felt rushed. I also felt ushered out. And I felt like she put in those tests just to appease me.

Then, I felt my sense of urgency turn to anxiety. Instead of me just taking the steps God had ordered, I tried to skip steps. I was stressing myself out, which I later learned can contribute to other issues. See, this is what you get when you rush God: fear and anxiety. This was one of the early hints of his dark humor. Well, I wasn't laughing! My whole life is on hold. Ugh... *Go away, Clarence!*

CHAPTER 3

WHEN DOVES CRIED

Can you remember a time the world stopped?

A question that is often asked about life-changing or historical events is "Where were you when...?" While people are specific about life events such as falling in love or learning about a death in the family, when I'm asked about the day I was diagnosed, my response is two-fold and is so detailed, it's almost creepy. I have the same detailed recollection of historical events such as 9/11 because, like my diagnosis, those were days the world stopped. I am sure I'm not alone in my attention to detail. Well, maybe I am a little.

On Tuesday, September 11, 2001, I experienced the day the world stopped. While on my way to class, just as I exited the highway around 8:15 a.m., I heard Harris Faulkner, a local news anchor, interrupt the morning radio show to share breaking news. I always got to campus an hour early on Tuesdays and Thursdays so I could eat breakfast. At 8:32 a.m., just as I was about to sit, still holding the tray with my omelet, the second plane hit. I remember a girl I didn't know standing behind me saying, "Oh my god, my brother works in one of those buildings! I have to call my parents!" To this day, I still have no idea who she was.

This was the first time I experienced the day the world stopped. My parents compared it to the days Kennedy and King were assassinated. When world-stopping events happen, you don't realize it in the moment; you remember the most mundane details about that day. My response to those questions of "Where were you when...?" are effortless, but two responses to the same question was a bit unusual.

I never thought Thursday, April 21, 2016, would be one of those days I would be asked about for the rest of my life. I also never thought I would be preparing to hear the worst news imaginable. The gravity of that date made me think of my childhood and how it played an important role in how proactive I was about my health. Even until this day, I have family members who will wait until they are *sick* sick before seeing a doctor. I refused to be reactive and on that fateful day, I understood why.

My first six years of life was spent living in a multigenerational home with my grandparents, aunts, uncles, and cousins. My grandfather was an assistant pastor at a Pentecostal church in Kansas City, MO and retired government security guard. He instilled faith in God in all of us. My grandmother was a homemaker who never worked outside the home. My family described her as spoiled because my grandfather made sure she never wanted for anything.

Both of the grandparents I grew up with had health issues, specifically diabetes and high blood pressure. I never realized the impact their very different approaches to health had on me until I learned of my own diagnosis. My grandfather was diligent about his health, but my grandmother did the bare minimum. Granddaddy went for long walks collecting cans throughout the neighborhood and ate breakfast, lunch, and dinner pretty much at the same time every day. We were the only house on the block with a full garden in the backyard because my grandaddy grew up on a farm and loved growing his own veggies. After my grandmother passed away, he would send his home health nurses out to pick greens, green beans, tomatoes, and okra.

I remember him calling out to my grandmother in the kitchen, "Bert, you pick those greens yet?"

"Yes, AJ, me and the kids went out and picked 'em," she yelled back. By kids, she meant me and my sister, Tianna.

"Uh... All right now. You don't want 'em going bad," he would add on.

"I know, AJ!" she said. We ate greens almost every Sunday at my grandparents' house.

My grandmother never deprived herself of a trip to Red Lobster or a lunch buffet. She was an OG foodie. Grandmother would make a whole dinner for my granddaddy and uncle, but would go out to eat with her friends. Some of my favorite memories of my grandmother were her impromptu lunch outings after picking me up from school early or taking us shopping and then to her favorite lunch buffet at Furr's or Shoney's. Unfortunately, those all-you-can-eat outings took a toll on her health. She suffered for a little more than a year, in and out of the hospital and at all-day dialysis treatments.

At the end of Grandmother's life, the doctor explained that when they found the source of one part of her illness, something else went wrong. Eventually, her body gave out, and on May 3, 1994, my seventy-one year old grandmother, Alberta Jesse Jackson Ponder, was called home to glory. I was fourteen years old, one month away from my eighth-grade graduation. Ironically, one month after my 1998 high school graduation, on July 12, my grandfather, Elder Aaron Jefferson Ponder, Sr. passed away from heart failure. He was eighty-one years old. My family always felt that my grandmother came to get him or that he was tired of living without her.

We made the most out of the four years we spent with just my grandfather, but when he passed away, it gave us comfort to know that Bert and AJ were together again. While writing this book, I realized my grandmother showed me what not to do and my grandfather showed me what to do when it came to my health. If I learned anything from the way my grandparents lived and died, it's that it's better to be proactive than reactive. As soon as my PCP said I would have to make the appointments for the mammogram, ultrasound, and MRI, I knew I had to call as soon as possible.

After discovering Clarence, it seemed as if the world slowed for two weeks and then stopped. I made several attempts at coming to peace with my impending diagnosis, but every time I went there, I thought about my family and upbringing. I didn't want to be another person hiding their illness or refusing to research treatments and outcomes. As I reflect on the day my world stopped, I remember almost every detail.

I was able to make an appointment for an ultrasound and mammogram for Thursday, April 21, 12:30 p.m. The sun was shining and it was pleasantly warm. I figured, after my appointment, I would grab a sandwich at Potbelly and have plenty of time to eat and check email before my student meetings started at 4 p.m. I loved that routine!

This was one of the earliest jokes by God on my journey. I got dressed for my meetings later that afternoon. Since I hadn't spoken with anyone about this appointment, I even put on deodorant. That was a funny lesson learned. I wore black slacks and blazer and one of my favorite blouses. It was a sleeveless, fuchsia top with black lace overlapping the front and a mid-waist belt. I didn't have a clear understanding of how to prepare for a mammogram nor ultrasound. God could have sent a smoke signal or something!

As I was walking from my car to Howard Hospital and arrived at the School of Medicine, I received a call from my cousin, Zester. The call interrupted my optimistic thought process. What if this is a cyst? What if it is benign? Well, God, definitely did not want me thinking about that, 'cause the phone rang. Ha!

"Hey, Neosh! They said Prince died," he said in a tone of disbelief.

I sat down on the short wall in front of the School of Medicine. The news knocked me off my feet.

"Huh? What? Wait... Zest, I found a lump in my boob and I'm literally on my way to have my breast checked," I said, plus I was annoyed. I mean they have been killing Prince since the '90s, but it was always false reports.

"I'm watching TMZ and they just announced it, but it's not confirmed. Do you know if it's true?"

Really? Talk about bad timing! Why do people call me like I am Google or Info(dot)com? I was annoyed 'cause there are always reports of people dying and my day is already stressful and now this.

"Okay, let me check Twitter. If it's not on Twitter then it's probably not true," I responded.

As I was checking Twitter, I couldn't help but think, of course today would be the day it would be true.

"So, you on your way to the doctor for your breast?" Zester asked.

"Yes, but please don't tell anyone. I'm just getting it checked. I don't want to worry anyone right now," I said.

"Oh okay, I won't tell anyone. I hope you're okay," he said.

"Nope, Prince isn't trending! So, it's probably fake. You know how they do. They kill Prince once a year since Mike. Thanks, Zes, I hope so too. I will keep you posted."

"Oookay, I'll talk to you later," he said before hanging up.

It was about 12:10 p.m., so I had plenty of time to walk the one block to the hospital and get checked in. By the time I reached the back entrance to the hospital, there was a buzz amongst people. I heard people saying "Oh my god!" and "Did you hear? Is it true?"

When I got to the front desk of the Breast Imaging Center, the first thing I was asked was, "Did you hear about Prince, the singer? He died!" I could tell the woman was in shock 'cause she tried to have a whole conversation with me about it. I tried, but I had to interrupt her.

"Hi, I am here for my 12:30 appointment. Last name Ponder," I said.

"Oh yes, Neo... Say your name for me?" she said in a thick island accent.

"Yes, Neosho Ponder."

"Okay, gotcha. Wait... You're thirty-six? What you doin' getting a mammogram at thirty-six?" she exclaimed rhetorically.

"Ma'am, that is none of your business. I have a golf ball in my boob and I really need it looked at!" I felt a tremble in my voice. I don't know if I was annoyed with her comfortability or just anxious to get this test done. It was probably both, but I was also trying not to receive the death of his Purple Majesty. I mean, crap, just throw the whole day away!

When I was called back, a really nice tech greeted me and instructed me to step into a room and remove my shirt only and put the gown on.

"How are you feeling, Ms. Ponder?" she asked.

"I'm fine. Just processing everything, you know," I responded.

"I understand. Okay, here you go. You're not wearing deodorant, are you?"

"Yeah, I always do. Was I..." I began to ask.

"Oh, no, ma'am, you can't wear deodorant," she said.

"Oh wow... I didn't know. I hadn't told anyone I was coming. Do I have to reschedule?" I asked.

She responded with a supportive chuckle, "You're fine, honey. Just go to that room there and wash your underarms. It happens all the time."

I felt so relieved. I was already anxious.

My breasts were not large, so it was difficult to get them between the cold, metal plates. As I am only five foot two, the tech and I both laughed at me struggling to put my barely C-cup on the plate and standing on my tiptoes at times to position myself. Then, I had to hold my breath and not move, while standing on my tiptoes with my boob barely on the plate. Talk about awkward coordination!

"Okay, Ms. Ponder, I think we have it," she said.

"Oh, thank god!" I said as I exhaled.

I was then instructed to walk down the hall to the ultrasound room. As I headed down the hall, the tech asked me a question: a specific, everyday question that proved to change the trajectory of this day.

"Oh, Ms. Ponder, do you want the doctor to look at these now or do you want her to call you?"

"Oh, um... she can call me. It's fine," I responded without thinking.

I am not sure why I was so easy breezy in that moment, especially when I was all anxious and ready to fight just a week prior. I think it was the lack of urgency from my primary care physician and just trying to get to my meetings with my students. It was almost two at this point, so I knew I still had the ultrasound and it would take too long for the radiologist to look at the film and then talk to me. I just wanted to move on with my day.

After the extremely uncomfortable mammogram, which I didn't know would also be painful, I walked down the hall for the ultrasound where I met another pleasant tech. The ultrasound tech was from Romania and so sweet. She asked me to lay down on the table.

And then, a woman burst into the room and moved the tech out of the way, "Hello, Ms. Ponder, I'm Dr. Brown-Hill. I am going to do your ultrasound today, okay?" she said in a commanding voice. She was a petite, light-skinned Black woman with short, natural hair.

"Okay, that's fine," I said. Typically, a tech does the mammograms and ultrasounds. But I mean I didn't have much of a choice.

As she put the gel on the ultrasound wand and moved it around my breast, she rambled, or so I thought. What I didn't know is that she was really concerned about what she saw on the mammogram.

She showed me Clarence on the monitor, then she checked my armpit and found a lump there. All I could think was "I'm ready to fight," but still I remained calm... I was almost serene.

"Oh, okay, see here," she said, referring to Clarence. "Now let me check... Okay, you have a fatty lymph node here as well. Okay. Let me just check the other breast also," she continued.

When she finished, she confirmed my age again and then asked about any family history with breast cancer. I gave her the same responses I'd given everyone else. "Thirty-six. No, no family history."

I think she picked up on how cool and calm I was. I told her my doctor was not alarmed and said since I don't have a family history, then there was probably nothing to worry about. In a hasty voice, she asked who my doctor was, whom she knew very well, and told the tech to get my doctor on the phone. Then she ordered a mammogram of my other breast and proceeded with the ultrasound of my right breast.

Everything was moving so fast. I hadn't *really* processed the situation and the doctor could tell. She then explained that after reviewing my mammogram, she was concerned because of my age and no family history. My calm, distant demeanor probably alarmed her because she instantly went from being a doctor to being one of those older women in church. I was still laying on the ultrasound table and in a very stern, yet concerned tone, she said, "Uh-uh, sit up."

When I sat up, I was very nonchalant. Then she took my hands into hers and asked me two questions I will never forget:

"Are you Christian?"

"Do you have family here?"

I immediately started sobbing. I hadn't told anyone about the lump, especially my family. I think that is when reality hit me and I...*broke...down.*

I wasn't crying because she was basically telling me my life would never be the same; I had already had those thoughts after touching Clarence for two weeks. I was crying because I realized in that moment, I would have to tell my Mama that I have breast cancer. I would have to tell my biological father that another one of his children has cancer. I would have to explain this to my nephews and niece. I had a responsibility to my family. It was crushing that those responsibilities might never be fulfilled.

While Dr. Brown-Hill could not officially confirm until the biopsy results came back, she told me she had been doing this for more than thirty years and it didn't look good. However, she assured me that with faith and prayer, I would get through it. While I appreciated her words of comfort, all I could think about was my mama and how this news was going to kill her.

As an ode to Prince's song, "When Doves Cry," I found comfort and understanding in the dichotomy of that day. According to songfacts.com (2021), Prince wrote this song for his Oscar winning film, *Purple Rain* and the phrase "when doves cry" is a metaphor for peace being broken. Now, when someone asks me, "where were you when you heard Prince died," I will respond with, "That was the day when doves cried." While the world was mourning his Purple Majesty, I was having multiple tests done to confirm a woman's worst fear. #RIPPrince

I need to take a detour here. When you hear those dreadful words, "you have cancer" or in my case, "I've been doing this for more than thirty years. I know what I see." I began to process what I heard. How did I come to be this person? What made me, *me?*

CHAPTER 4

THE MAKINGS OF ME

———

Ahead of my final reconstructive surgery in May 2021, the anesthesiologist called a timeout, which means he asked me my full name and date of birth. Well, since I was delirious from lack of sleep and them trying to start an IV for almost three hours, my responses were, let's say, unexpected.

"Time out," said the anesthesiologist.

"Time out," replied the nurses, like call and response.

"Please state your name and date of birth," he asked me.

Without thinking, I immediately responded with,

"My first name is a city in southwest Missouri, my middle name was a station wagon, and my last name means, 'to think.'"

"Was that the time out?" a nurse asked.

"I guess so," the anesthesiologist said.

"Oh, and I was born Sunday, March 9, 1980, The National Holiday, around 4:30 a.m. "Crazy Little Thing Called Love" was number one on the charts by my favorite band. That's how I know Freddie was meant to be my friend," I continued.

"Wow, was all of that true?" the nurse asked.

"Oh, Pam is special. She got my first name off a road sign and middle name off a station wagon, while stuck in traffic," I said, dazed and confused.

The entire surgical staff was entertained and confused. I also believed they were intrigued by my cool-ass name and interesting details of how I described my name and date of birth. I probably will never see any of them again, but remembering that hilarious time out made me think about how I came to be *me*. Paraphrasing the incomparable Curtis Mayfield, these are the makings of me.

Throughout this book, you will see that I call my parents by their first names and titles interchangeably. That is a family thing that I will elaborate on a bit more later. For now, just as an FYI, Pam gave birth to me and is my mama, Gene is my biological father, and Rodger is my dad, the parent God sent us, and he has been married to Pam for thirty-three years. I had a fairly well-rounded parental unit, as well as extended family who stepped in when needed. I am a firm believer in the African Proverb, "It takes a village to raise a child."

What I love most about my parents is they each had a role and played their positions well. My dads, Gene and Rodger, never stepped on each other's toes or exchanged negative words regarding my upbringing. Heck, they got along better than my biological parents. It was not until I was an adult that I recognized the mutual respect they had for one another. They were both pleasant, non-temperamental men who always got along with everyone, so their convos over a beer on the porch before my weekend visits with Gene makes even more sense.

Gene seemed to defer all traditional child-rearing to Pam. She always included Rodger in decisions regarding our discipline, permissions, and celebrations. When reflecting on my earliest memories, I realized Pam never approached mother-hood as a single parent, which was an aha moment! Despite being a single woman for the first seven years of my life, Pam always had a village. I learned so much from my parents and extended family, which allowed me to be independent, opinionated, and forward-thinking. My three parents were always there to guide me, but they never forced me to be someone God did not create me to be. I am definitely the product of all three of my parents and by-product of the village.

Pam had been taking care of kids since she was teenager. Her two older sisters, Renee and Sheliah, both had babies twice at the same time. It's okay to read that again for clarity. Yes, my aunties, who I affectionately call my second and third mamas, were pregnant at the same time in 1969 (girls) *and* 1970 (boys). It's weird, but super cool at the same time! Pam was about sixteen years old when she became an auntie and live-in babysitter. Renee and Sheliah worked full-time and since they all lived at home, the kids were with Pam the majority of the time. My older cousins spent so much time with Pam, they began to call her mama. She corrected them and said she is Pam, not mama.

For some strange reason, my aunties instructed their young children to call them by their first names, Renee and Sheliah. When my cousins heard everyone in the house call my grandparents "Mama" and "Daddy," they began to use those same titles. It was natural for me to call my mama "Pam" and my grandmother "Mama." Pam never cared what we called her as long as we knew who was our "mama." Apparently, titles were not needed for some members of my family, but as more generations have come, titles have become terms of endearment, such as my younger cousins calling my parents, "Auntie Pam" and "Uncle Rodger."

Since she didn't think she could conceive naturally, Pam was somewhat of a professional auntie until I came along. I think that is where I get my super auntie ways from. *I get it from my mama!* We—my younger sister, Tianna, and I—were blessed to have a first-time mom with a live-in village and so much experience taking care of children. Honestly, I'm glad she had my four older cousins, Shayn, Tina, Zester, and Terry, to practice on. They low-key resented us because we took their fun auntie from them, but I'm sure they were excited to have two little ones to cuddle with and pick on.

Pam was two weeks away from her twenty-seventh birthday when she gave birth to me. One of my favorite stories of my birth was that since she was in labor for so long, nineteen hours to be exact, Pam helped Sheliah study for her business college exam. As I was preparing to enter the world, I was listening to my mama help her sister study. As a result of those long hours of walking the hospital hallways, Sheliah earned the highest grade in her class: an A+. Just as Pam and Sheliah were extremely different, so were me and Tianna.

I spent thirteen glorious months as an only child and then Tianna came along, messing... I mean, *blessing* us. I think Pam needed two of us, because we could not be with her by ourselves! I always use the hashtag, #SheCrazyButSheMine, to describe Pam. The word crazy is colloquial for interesting, comical, and fun. Pam is definitely one of a kind! However, I don't know what I would have done without my sister, Tianna. God is funny like that, isn't He? I mean, Pam went from not thinking she could have kids to having two babies in thirteen months. Thankfully, she was two and done. To paraphrase the Bible, "No more room at the inn."

I love that we are Irish Twins, my sister and me, but ironically, we could not be less alike! We are like oil and water. She is tall; I am short. She is right-handed; I am left-handed. She was athletic, but didn't know anything about sports. I was not physically athletic, but understood and loved watching sports. She was like a tomboy who loved wearing dresses. I was more of a girly girl who loved wearing Jordan sneakers and baggy jeans. Probably our biggest difference was how I always excelled at school. Tianna hated school, probably because she struggled academically. I think her favorite thing about school was that she could borrow my clothes and shoes. Now, she was roughly four inches taller than me at this time, and her feet were about a half size larger as well. Like most siblings with little in common, we fought like cats and dogs. Of course, we would make up because she needed something from me and as the older sibling, I obliged.

Despite our differences, I don't think I could have grown up without a sibling. Tianna was my first student. I taught her how to tie her shoes, ride a bike, and always helped with her homework. I grew to be a bit protective of her after she was hit by a car at two years old. The driver performed CPR and revived her. Due to her injuries, the doctor said she may not be able to have children. Well, life is funny like that and by life, I mean God. He blessed her with five children. When Tianna became a mom, I fell into my role as auntie. Being an auntie is one of my favorite roles in life and I am good at it!

Growing up as one of the youngest in a multi-generational household, you see so many ways to approach life. As an adult, I gravitated toward my grandfather's level of commitment and involvement in church. My Christian foundation began with my grandparents and when I was diagnosed with breast cancer, I tapped into my roots. My faith shifted immensely! I don't know where I would be if I did not have that solid Christian foundation. My unwavering faith is also why I laugh at God laughing at me! Like the old saying goes, "wanna make God laugh? Tell him your plans!" And then there are His own words, "For I know the plans I have for you [...]" in Jeremiah 29:11. The Christian foundation instilled in me as a child and the street smarts Pam taught us were essential to my childhood, but unbeknownst to me, there was more.

God knew exactly what I needed to round out my trifecta of parents. I gave thanks almost daily for the blessing of three parents for twenty-eight of my forty-one years. My biological father, Gene, suddenly passed away at the most inopportune time. I will unpack the humor in losing my father in a later chapter. While the past five years have been difficult at times, I am blessed to still have my parents, Pam and Rodger, who celebrated thirty-three years of marriage while writing this book.

As much as I loved living with my whole family at 4101, my grandparents address, all three of us—Pam, Tianna, and me—needed Rodger. He gave Pam balance, protection, and stability. He gave us guidance, discipline, and sooo many tools to get through life. Together, Pam and Rodger kept us fed, clothed, safe, and entertained, but leaving 4101, the only home I'd ever known, was not easy. A cancer diagnosis really forces you to reflect and put things into perspective.

Of course, at seven years old you don't know what is good for you, but I did not want to leave the only home I had known. I pretty much skipped first-grade by spending most of my school day in a second-grade class. So, when we moved across state lines into the state of Kansas over the summer, Pam enrolled us in the neighborhood school for the 1987–1988 school year. Apparently, Kansas does not place students according to academic abilities or test scores.

If you are seven years old, you are in second grade. *Full stop.* I blamed Rodger for taking us away. A year after Pam moved us in with Rodger, they were married. Nope, she didn't even ask us! We just had to go along with it. The nerve!

When Pam and Rodger told my grandfather they had gotten married, he said, "I need to see the marriage license." When they returned with their proof of marriage, granddaddy looked at Pam and said, "Do what he says." He then looked at Rodger and said, "Don't put your hands on her." My grandfather's advice may have been a bit antiquated, but that was his way of giving his approval and sharing what he believed makes a healthy marriage. Clearly it worked!

My only ally about the Rodger situation was Grandmother. She did *not* like Rodger one bit and I loved it! I was a "run-tell-that" kid when it came to my mama's husband and the way he did things. I laugh at those things now, but as an eight-year-old kid, it was the worst. He disciplined us for arguing and fighting, no matter who started it. He made us say "Yes, sir" and "Yes, ma'am" to grown-ups. We even had to sit at the table and eat together, oh but not before washing our hands. *The audacity!* I would tell Grandmother everything!

I remember the calls to Pam going off about what I had told her and then, of course, I would get the Black mama speech of "what happens in this house, stays in this house."

When I was nine, we briefly moved back home to 4101. When I say, "we," I mean all of us: me, Tianna, Pam, *and* Rodger. We lived with my grandparents, uncles, and cousin for four months until we moved into a house. During that time, my grandparents saw what Pam saw in Rodger. They did not have to fix anything in the house. Even when my grandmother was nasty toward him, he still called them Mom and Pops and responded to them with "sir" and "ma'am." I also became accustomed to him being there. By the time we moved out, after just four months, my grandmother *loved* Rodger! No one could say one thing negative about her favorite (and only) son-in-law. I believe she saw what everyone saw in Rodger. Despite him being the size of an offensive lineman, the football position he played in college, Rodger was a gentle soul. He was extremely respectful, kind, fun, intelligent, and is a man of integrity. He wore Grandmother down by being himself and taking care of her daughter and granddaughters.

Rodger was a family man through and through, which comes from his working-class values and massive, close-knit family. When I say Rodger has an enormous family, that is an understatement. While his mother was having ten kids, his eldest sister was also having ten kids! Rodger is the youngest boy and has one sister younger than him. He married his first wife while still in college and they had a son, *little* Rodger. The marriage lasted only three years, but I believe he learned a lot about himself and what it takes to be a good husband and father. Our families were already connected because Rodger's nephew was in a long-term relationship with Pam's first cousin. They already had a daughter and would later marry. So, I have always known Rodger, but I would have never imagined the role he would play in my life as my dad.

It took two years for me to realize that I could not live without my dad. While I spent some weekends, holidays, and breaks with Gene, Rodger was home for me. I was about ten years old when I shared that if they get a divorce, I want to live with him. That does not mean I didn't love my mama and sister. It meant that I could not live in the house without him being there. Lucky for me, we never had to cross that bridge.

As I got older, I began to understand why Rodger was sent to us by God. When my mama and sister did not understand some of my life's curve balls, Rodger did. When Pam was reluctant to help with my financial aid paperwork in college, Rodger explained why I needed the help. I realized in college that my lifestyle was veering away from my mama and sister. I began to outgrow my family and Rodger was the only one I could talk to without having to alter my vernacular. We became so close that we could have a whole conversation with a look, which began to annoy Pam and irritate Tianna. It was like our little nuclear family was split down the middle. We would usually laugh and tell them to calm down. Rodger and I were a team! Now, when Tianna and Pam disagree on something, we step in as mediators. And of course, we would look at each other, shake our heads, and laugh.

By the time I moved away from Kansas City in 2005, Rodger's faith in God noticeably increased. He led my mama back to church and now, he is a deacon and Pam is an usher. Our lengthy phone conversations usually end with Rodger saying, "All right, baby. Talk to you later. Love you. God bless." His faith and prayer helped get me through many difficult moments in life. While my dad is not perfect, he is perfect for my mama and God's gift to me and Tianna.

CHAPTER 5

NDA: *NEOSHO* DISCLOSURE AGREEMENT

"I can't wait to tell my family about my *cancer!*" said no one.

What they do say is, "I can't wait to tell my family about my new boyfriend," or "I can't wait to tell my family about my job offer."

By thirty-five, I figured I'd have my PhD and be making amazing contributions to the world. I planned to buy a house before forty and if not dating, be in a relationship leading to marriage. I also was excited about traveling, especially since I had an unstamped passport. In the US, to be young, gifted, and Black with your soul intact was the dream. Educated Black women in their mid-thirties are expected to settle down with a family, be an agent of change, or live it up on "vacay" (or *bae*cay: vacay with your bae). Who wouldn't want to share any of that with their family and friends? Well, instead of telling my parents about an amazing guy I was seeing or an impactful article I wrote, I was trying to figure out how to tell them I had cancer.

Lawd, what would Pam say or do? I knew she wouldn't take the news well. Pam is the type that falls to the floor crying when she hears bad news. See, my mama is not an optimist: that's my dad. She will *fall out* thinking her baby is about to die! Rodger would have to remind Pam that God has me and that I would be okay. My heart was pounding. My spirit was confused. My soul wept for what they would go through as parents.

As I was walking to my car having just received my diagnosis, my legs felt like Jell-o. It was the longest walk ever! My mind was all over the place, more than usual. I needed prayer, so I called Denise, my friend from church. Denise was in seminary and is a prayer warrior. I shared with her that I felt a lump and it was just "unofficially" confirmed and I needed to tell my parents. She prayed with me and then advised me to tell them gently. She suggested I start off with a joke or something to lighten the mood. I mean this isn't a "knock, knock" kind of moment, but hey, I needed all the help I could get. So, I practiced!

"Knock, knock."

"Who's there?"

"Breast."

"Breast? What the... Breast who?"

"Breast cancer!"

Nah, I didn't think that type of joke would work for this situation. As I was driving home from the hospital, I was disheveled, but one thing that stayed at the forefront of my mind was, "Damn. I haven't begun to live. Really, God? Really? This has to be a joke... Ha ha... God's got jokes!"

It was about 7:30 p.m. when I gathered enough strength to make the call. I wanted to be prepared for questions, but I knew the hardest part was about to happen. Telling Pam that "the one who's been with you the longest" is sick and there is nothing she can do about it was the hardest thing I had to do. I had no appetite and besides a few sips of water to get rid of cotton mouth, I had not eaten or drank anything all day. I mean, who thinks to eat when they are already digesting the worst news of their life? Denise prayed with me. I prayed with me. Finally, I had to figure out how to say it, so I came up with the Neosho Disclosure Agreement (NDA).

My dad answered the phone, "Hey baby!"

I replied, "Hey! What y'all doin?"

He said, "Oh nothin'. Just watching TV."

I asked if they both were in the room and he said Pam had just walked in. I asked if their door was shut. He said yes.

I took a deep breath and said, "I wanted to talk to y'all and don't want Tianna and the kids to hear me."

He said, "It's just me and your mom."

I said, "On April 8, at 5:37 p.m., I felt a lump in my left breast. I had a mammogram and ultrasound, and the doctor is pretty sure it is breast cancer."

There was a deafening silence. I said, "Rodger, pick Pam up off the floor."

He said, "Yeah, she is crying. She just ran out of the room."

I knew she would take it hard. She isn't as strong as she appears. When Pam came back in the room, she said, "Neosho..." still crying a bit.

I said, "It's okay. I am scheduled for a biopsy to confirm everything, so I don't want to tell anyone until after that."

"We will be praying everything goes well. Just remember, God is the top physician. We will be praying and make sure you call us after," he said.

Pam asked, still in tears, "Who is going with you?"

"Rhonda and my friend from church, Denise," I said.

They both said, "Okay, good. You won't be by yourself. We love you."

I said, "I love y'all too. Please don't tell anyone until after I find out more info on Monday."

"We won't" he said.

I said, "Pam? *Don't tell Tianna, please!*"

She said, "I won't, baby, promise."

We got off the phone and I basically cried myself to sleep. My first NDA was delivered, which was a *woosah* moment. It can only get easier from here, but what is easy when you are disclosing the worst news of your life?

When your life is on the line, you begin to think about all the things you haven't done. I have never been in love with someone who loved me back; I had never conceived a child; I had never traveled outside of the United States; I had never owned a home, and the list went on. I was just getting ready to begin my adult life. I dedicated seven years of my young adulthood to ensuring I didn't have to struggle financially and make a meaningful impact on society. Instead, I was diagnosed with Stage 2B invasive ductal carcinoma at thirty-six years old. Talk about two things that don't go together!

I wasn't upset, scared, or angry yet. I was ready to fight because the way my faith is set up, He didn't bring me this far to leave me. While I was ready to fight this disease, my faith didn't prepare me for the battles ahead.

I slowly began disclosing to my family and friends, but quickly realized how difficult it was to tell someone you love that you have cancer. So, I figured if I told one person on each side of my family, then word would travel. I figured if I did a conference call with my line sisters, sorority sisters who pledge with you, then I wouldn't have to tell my big sisters, the older sorority sisters. Well, that was easier said than done. I kept asking myself, "*how do I do this?*"

It was my story to tell and I get that, but the Neosho Disclosure Agreement always involved the receiver asking if I needed anything or specifics about treatment when I didn't have all of the information. Typically, a non-disclosure agreement protects the person requiring it to be signed. Well in my case, the Neosho Disclosure Agreement was just a way to disclose this news without me leaving anything out and helping me keep my emotions intact, 'cause it was hard, y'all.

The night before my biopsy, I invited Desmond over. We tried dating, but were on a break and had not been intimate since mid-March. He was the only person besides myself who had touched my breasts in more than a year. I asked him to touch my left breast. When he touched it, he felt Clarence and jumped back in terror.

"Oh my god, Neosho..." he gasped, as his voice quivered.

"Have you felt that before?" I asked.

"No... *No!* You... What..." He attempted to speak.

"Yes, it is a tumor. I call it Clarence. I am trying to see how long it's been there," I said.

"When did you... How long have you felt it?" he asked.

"I adjusted my boob in my tank top a couple of weeks ago and there it was. I figured since you're the only other person who has touched my breasts in over a year, maybe you'd felt it. I'm just trying to figure out how long it had been there," I said.

"Yeah, I never felt that. Are you good? I mean, considering."

"I mean, I know what it is, but tomorrow's biopsy will confirm it," I said.

After disclosing to Desmond, I grew more and more strategic about who, when, and how I delivered the NDA. I had to prioritize the family members I told, such as my sister and nephews knowing before my aunties and cousins. My auntie, Sheliah, told my mama's side of the family, except my cousin, Tina. Tina is the most dramatic person in our family. She takes everything hard, so they were concerned about how she would take it. All of this, unbeknownst to me, was going on while I was grappling with what happens after the biopsy. My family was literally going back and forth about who would tell Tina. It was hilarious! Then, one day, I was leaving the movie theater, and I received a text that read, "If you die, bitch, I'll kill you." I burst into a gut-busting laugh! Heck, I still laugh when I think about it. Tina would bring the comic relief I needed.

I know you are wondering why I would laugh so hard at such an offensive text and why would someone send it in the first place. Well, two things. One: you clearly are not familiar with that line. Two: you clearly are not a movie watcher. Both of which are fine, because I was overjoyed by the text. To this day, that was *by far* the best response to hearing about my diagnosis and it came from the one person who would say something like that. Like I said, my dramatic, crazy cousin, Tina, takes news like this very hard. Growing up, our family loved movies, especially movies about musical artists. Well, in this case, she quoted a family favorite, *What's Love Got To Do With It* (1993) and it was perfect! I could not have asked for a better response. I know that sounds weird, but it is the Ponder family humor. Now, my sister's response was just as surprising, but nothing compares to Tina.

Unfortunately, I did not get to tell my sister because she was included on a text message about my biopsy and learned of my cancer from my landlord updating my parents via text. I really didn't want to tell close friends and family until I had more answers to the barrage of questions. I also needed to make sure I had energy to deal with the sadness and be receptive of all the prayers and advice. When Tianna called me, I was intentionally brief because I didn't want to scare her about what I could possibly go through and while I never thought I would die, my sister (and family) definitely did.

"Hey, T," I said.

"Hey, what is this text about?" she asked with concern and confusion in her voice. "Why is Rhonda texting me about..."

"Well, she didn't know that I hadn't told you yet," I jumped in and cleared up.

"What's goin' on, Sissy?" she asked calling me her term of endearment for a sister.

As I delivered the NDA, I was worried about how she would handle the news.

"So, you just felt it...in your boob and then went to the doctor?"

"Yup. When I felt it, I knew."

"You knew? How? I mean, are they sure?"

"God told me this is why I can't find a job 'cause he has a bigger job for me."

"Oh wow...so now what? You did the biopsy, so what does that do?"

"A biopsy is to test the tissue of the tumor to see if it's cancer," I said.

"Aw, okay, so now what? Oh, you gon' lose your titties? Aww... Your little boobies," she said with a laugh.

"Girl, they are not that little. And yeah, more than likely I will have a double mastectomy," I quipped.

"So, what about kids,' cause I been patient with your schoolin' and now you done, Imma need you to get on my niece or nephew!"

"Girl! I am not thinking about that!" I exclaimed.

"I know, I know, Sissy! I'm just playin'! I just know you wanna have a baby of your own," she said.

Her acknowledging that really touched me. I never thought she really cared about me having kids since I had been so involved in helping her raise hers. We have always had a tumultuous relationship, even to this day, but we only have each other. I have to remind her: "we all we got!" It is only the two of us. Pam only got pregnant twice. Even though Tianna has an older sister from her biological father and I have three older siblings from my biological father, all of whom are at least ten years older, we only had each other growing up. I had always been thankful for my sister.

After speaking to my sister, I called my Uncle Gary, Gene's younger brother, who was more like my surrogate father. I shared the news with him and his wife, Aunt Anita. I asked them to tell Gene and Victor, my older brother who had been living with multiple myeloma since 2007. Since he was on more than 50 percent oxygen, I was not sure how he would receive the news, but I did not have it in me to tell them. So, Uncle Gary said he would and I said would call Vincent, my eldest brother who lived in Los Angeles. Surprisingly, they all took it very well and Gene began to call and check on me regularly. It was pretty cool, since he was not a phone person. I believe it was due to his severe stutter, but his calls meant a lot.

Honestly, delivering my NDAs was extremely difficult, however it allowed me to see how strong, weak, and supportive people were. So, instead of telling *all* of Facebook, in early May I decided to create a secret Facebook group with the cover photo that said "Dear cancer, you suck." I began to add people to the group, which at its height reached about 220 people. I didn't post anything. I just kept adding people. I added people I trusted with the biggest news of my life, family, close friends, and sorors. The next thing I knew, I was getting calls from people I hadn't spoken to in a while!

They were confused and wondered what the cover photo meant. At first, I was like, "What cover photo? Oh that! Chile, they tryin' to say I got the cancer 'cause I discovered Clarence in my boob."

"Clarence? Who is that?" I was asked.

"My annoying-ass tumor!"

"Why you call it Clarence?" It was a logical question, but I name everything.

"Because Clarence was always that kid in school that got on everyone's nerves and this thang won't go away! So, its name is *Clarence*."

"Oh okay. Makes sense," they would always say with a laugh, except my one friend named... Yup, you guessed it: *Clarence*. He eventually understood my reasoning.

I had one friend that took my diagnosis harder than some of my family. That was becoming a trend that I was not emotionally ready to handle. I was still teaching at Howard and figuring out my treatment plan. I did not have the mental or emotional capacity to comfort people who were sad about *my* cancer diagnosis.

As the spring 2016 semester came to an end, I was slowly sharing my news via the Neosho Disclosure Agreement with my students and mentors. While sitting in my office at Howard, the Dean of the School of Communications stopped by for a visit. She asked me if I knew that President Obama was the commencement speaker and if I would like to attend as faculty. Without knowing what I was going through healthwise, the Dean asked me to join my former professors and now colleagues on The Yard, the grassy area of campus where the university commencement is held. It would be a historic commencement ceremony and I knew I would not be returning to Howard as an adjunct next year, so this was the perfect way to close this chapter of my life.

Commencement 2016 was amazing! I got to hear our "Forever POTUS," the forty-fourth President of the United States, Barack Obama, deliver the commencement address, but I also bore witness to an earth-shattering monologue from my soror, the incomparable Cicely Tyson. For one afternoon in May 2016, I forgot I was in for the fight of my life. For the first time since April 7, Clarence did not exist and then, while snapping pics with my mentors, the NDA popped in my head.

"They don't even know! How do I tell them?" I thought. I was still unsure and it took a while longer to disclose to my mentors, but I definitely had to tell Patricia.

I had agreed to teach at Trinity Washington University that summer. I needed to deliver an NDA to Dr. Patricia Love, my supervisor, sorority sister, and someone I really respected. I was nervous because I needed this job, but I could not work *this* summer. I prayed that she would understand and consider me for future semesters. We agreed to meet in her office, the week after commencement. When I arrived, she was just getting out of a meeting.

"Hey there! How are ya?" she asked in her boisterous voice.

"Mm, I'm okay. How are you?" I asked.

"Oh, girl, busy! The semester just ended and now we are gearing up for summer," she said.

"Understandable. Well, I wanted to chat with you..." I began.

I was afraid to tell her.

"Well..." I continued. "On Friday..." And as I delivered the NDA, she went from Dr. Love to Patricia, a concerned Black woman and soror. I didn't know what to expect.

"Oh my god, Neosho, I am so sorry!"

"Thanks. I am still processing it all. I'm not sure if I can still teach this summer. I realize that more than likely, I will either have a mastectomy or begin chemo treatment this summer."

"Oh of course, honey! Don't worry about it! You go take care of yourself, okay?"

"Yes, ma'am. I just... It's just a lot," I said with tears in my eyes. "I was just beginning to live or figure out what was next for me and now this."

"You focus on *you*. Let me know when you are ready to come back and teach. Your job will be here," she assured me.

I was beyond relieved! This was the conversation I dreaded because I loved teaching and Patricia always thought of me when classes opened up.

"Let me know if you need anything and keep me updated on how you're doing, okay?" she said.

"Okay, I will. Thank you. I really appreciate you!"

As I was leaving Trinity, I was thinking about how gracious Patricia was to me. I was also thinking about how I was afraid to have a scarlet letter on my head. I figured after how supportive Patricia was, that maybe others would be as well. I called my other soror who was the founder of a non-profit that trains and promotes Black women entrepreneurs. She was just as supportive and gracious as Patricia. The job I was scheduled to discuss with her was the perfect use of my PhD. The soror was adamant about me taking care of myself. I appreciated her understanding and encouragement. I realized the NDAs were working, but they were mentally and spiritually draining.

As the month of May came to a close, a majority of my family and friends knew about my diagnosis, but what I realized is that I was losing steam on telling people. One by one, people were learning of my condition. There was no shortage of offers of support...so I thought.

CHAPTER 6

A CHANGE IS GONNA COME

―――

My official diagnosis was invasive ductal carcinoma (IDC), Stage 2B, HER2+, ER/PR negative, and since at least one lymph node was also positive for cancer it meant... Drum roll, please... the left boob had to go.

The first cancer doctor I met with was my breast surgeon, Dr. Roberts. He explained that since my stage was low and I had no evidence of metastasis, I could do chemo first, which could shrink Clarence, then undergo surgery. Or if I wanted to do fertility treatment of freezing my eggs, I could wait on chemo and have surgery first. I had already decided to have the double mastectomy because I wanted my breasts to look alike. Despite the data saying otherwise, I also didn't want to worry about recurrence in my other breast or, as I put it: "I don't want to feed my future babies cancer milk." Well, once again, God had other plans.

Dr. Roberts introduced me to Gwen, the breast navigator, whose job was to support breast cancer patients as they go through surgery and treatment. Honestly, she was more than that! Gwen was a social worker, researcher, fundraiser, confidant, all the things. She was soft spoken, but super resourceful! We instantly connected. She loved my personality and how warm and open I was. I think I made her job easier because I was not overly emotional about my diagnosis. We also connected through our faith, which she explained is probably why I was not freaking out as one would expect. She orientated me on the job of a breast cancer patient and later, a survivor. Gwen was my north star. She accompanied me to my first meeting with the oncologist and sang his praises. When I was called into the exam room, she stayed in the waiting room. I figured she went to appointments with a lot of patients and didn't want to impose. I heard such great things about Dr. Patel from Dr. Roberts and Gwen, so I was confident and comfortable walking into the exam room.

Dr. Patel was my oncologist and an Indian-American with a heavy accent who wore a turban. Dr. Patel immediately eased my fears and comforted me just by how he showed up. I immediately impressed him by sharing that I knew that his turban represented his culture and Sikh religion, which I learned from an informative speech of one of my Howard University students. And wouldn't you know it, that same student attended his church! I believe it was fate that brought us together. He was so nice and extremely patient. I think he enjoyed having a patient familiar with research because he explained every aspect of my prognosis, answered every question, and showed me the data to back it up. I was concerned that his accent could present a communication barrier, but it never did. He never hesitated to repeat something or clarify his statements.

During our initial meeting, Dr. Patel laid the foundation of all options, which gave me a sigh of relief.

"Dr. Ponder..." he began.

"Oh no, please, call me Neosho," I laughed.

"No, no, you earned it, so I do not mind referring to you as doctor," he said.

"Well, I am fine with Neosho or Dr. Ponder. but not Ms. Ponder. That was my grandmother," I replied.

"Got it," he said with a smile, "You are in a very good place. Your tumor is small and you do not show signs of it being in any other part of your body, but you will have to have an MRI and PET scan to make sure. I am also going to order you a 3D mammogram so I can have a better look. You should be able to get it done today right upstairs."

Having a cancer survivor as a parent had its perks. Gene explained that I should always take a notebook when meeting with doctors, even if someone was with me. That was a lot to take in, but I was also taking notes. I was a little concerned because I was traveling in a few weeks to surprise Pam at her bowling tournament in Las Vegas and to see my family in Kansas City.

Dr. Patel explained that I do not have to rush and make a decision about the order of treatment.

"See here," he said as he showed me on the computer screen, "you are Stage 2B, meaning your cancer has not spread beyond your breast tissue and nearby lymph nodes to other parts of your body. And since you are HER2+ and negative for hormones, you have some time. So go on vacation; enjoy your family."

In that moment, I felt good about where I was. "Do you have any questions for me?" he asked.

I had two burning questions that concerned me more than losing my breasts or hair.

"Yes, I have two... Can I donate blood? I have a rare blood type..." He looked to see it, but before he could find it, I added, "It's AB+. I donate blood pretty regularly. I mean the Red Cross calls me for blood because we are the universal recipient," I continued, "but we can only donate to other AB+ people."

The whole truth is, the Red Cross called me like a bill collector! I would get automated messages about donating during the holidays and then real people the rest of the year.

"Yes, I am familiar. I see your concern. Well, that is good you know to donate, but unfortunately due to chemo, you won't be able to donate for at least five years. More than likely, you won't be able to donate again. I'm sorry," he said.

"It's fine. I figured I couldn't, but I wanted to confirm," I said.

"And your next question," he said.

"Oh, well... Will I be able to have babies after treatment?" I asked. I could tell that he noticed the fear and concern in my voice and on my face.

"Let's see, you are thirty-six. And you do not have children. Well, some patients with hormone positive cancers go into menopause..." he began.

"Yeah, but I am ER/PR negative, so that's a good thing, right?" I exclaimed.

"Well, yes, and you are HER2+, which means you have a direct treatment regimen, carboplatin, taxotere, and perjeta, plus a year of Herceptin. You have regular menstrual cycles, yes?" he asked.

"Yes, but I have PCOS as well, which is probably why I have never been pregnant," I said.

"Well, as long as chemo does not cause menopause, you should be fine. You are at an age where it could though, so I recommend freezing your eggs just in case," he said.

"Oh wow... Really? Okay, I will look into that."

"Do you know how much it will cost?" I asked, "I don't have money, like, at all," I said with an embarrassed chuckle.

"No, but there may be ways to pay for it," he said.

"Oh, okay, I'll ask Gwen," I said.

"Yes! Yes, she will help you," he immediately replied.

Before leaving his office, Dr. Patel told me I needed three things to get through this cancer journey, medication, a support system, and faith. It was a simple, yet profound statement that further confirmed that this was the oncologist I needed and the one I wanted. I don't know if he knew how strong my faith was at that time, but over the years we have witnessed the role my faith in God has had on not only my healing, but also the external hardships I have endured.

After leaving that appointment, I felt relieved and a newfound sense of hope for a future after all of this. By this time, I was still making peace with my decision to have a double mastectomy and thinking about resources to pay for my egg freezing, which is where the phenomenal Gwen comes in! Gwen gave me several resources and highly recommended a reputable fertility clinic. I decided to look into funding and take some time to pray about everything and enjoy my friends and family. I had planned a trip to surprise my mama while she was on a trip in Las Vegas and then from there, we were flying to Kansas City to spend time with the rest of the family.

My diagnosis made this trip even more meaningful because I could spend mother daughter time with Pam, which was rare. I definitely wish my sister would have come, but unfortunately couldn't make it. Pam was really glad to spend that time with me. After five amazing days in Vegas with Pam, we flew to KC. I had never spent that amount of alone time with my mama as an adult. Remember, I am only thirteen months older than Tianna.

It was pretty cool hanging with Pam. Since I had not lived with her in sixteen years, I was reminded that we are very different women, which made parts of the trip awkward and funny. Most people would tone down their wild ways when traveling with their parents, i.e., not drinking too much or partying too hard. Well, I think Pam toned down for me! I'm the square daughter. I don't drink much or gamble, so she didn't do those things. Now, I know my mama! She was on her best behavior with me, but if Tianna was there, Pam would have been like, *"turn down for what!"*

Once back in KC, I was able to hang out with all three sides of my family, take family pictures, and eat at all my favorite places. It also gave me a chance to answer questions about my condition. I explained my options and what I was thinking of doing. My sister was in support of what I wanted to do about fertility, but I think it was because she really wanted me to have a baby. I explained the cost associated with freezing my eggs and she asked if I considered adopting. Sometimes, I (affectionately) wonder how we are sisters. I lovingly reminded her of her brood of biological children and that I wanted the opportunity to carry my own baby just as she did. We laughed about it, but I still shake my head whenever she presses me about her being an auntie. I'm workin' on it, T! I'm workin' on it!

My Ponder family is comical in a crazy, inside-joke kind of way, which really made my visit meaningful. A few of them were even cool with touching Clarence! I am the only person in my family to be diagnosed with breast cancer, so I took this time to educate my family on the diagnosis process, including how I discovered Clarence. My cousin, Terry, asked if my butt had been checked for tumors because it looks swollen. These funny comments gave me comfort, just knowing they were all in my corner with laughter and prayers. We laughed a lot during those convos, especially reminiscing about our uncle, Junior, and grandparents. This is exactly what I needed to fuel me in this war against cancer.

Pam agreed to come back to DC with me and stay until I either had my surgery or started chemo. While it gave me comfort to have my mama there, I think it really gave her a renewed sense of purpose in my life. I was a precocious kid, responsible teen, and independent young woman, so up to this point, she had pretty much been a spectator in my life. I believe it gave her joy to have a front row seat and even play a role in my cancer journey. Pam is not naturally nurturing, but she supports me the best way she knows how. She came to every doctors appointment as I weighed my options and prepared for next steps. Now, I said she came to the appointments, which I loved, but I had to console her a few times. I felt bad, but at one appointment, she broke down crying and I asked if she needed to step into the hallway. In that moment, I had briefly forgotten the toll my diagnosis was taking on her, especially since I had not needed her for a very long time. There is nothing like a mother's love and despite a few bumps here and there, her being there was very comforting.

My final decision about the order of my treatment rested on whether I could freeze my eggs. Pam and I met with the fertility clinic about the possibility of freezing my eggs before chemo. This meeting was enlightening. While discussing the egg freezing process, Dr. Austin explained the BMI (body mass index) threshold for the procedure. I thought it was funny that I barely made the cutoff for approval and that was due to the cleanse I had done just after discovering Clarence. Now, if that ain't a punchline on one of God's jokes, I don't know what is!

"*Wow!*" I exclaimed, "so the BMI cutoff is forty and I am at a thirty-eight? My Lord..."

"What does that mean exactly?" Pam asked.

"It means that if I had not lost nearly fifteen pounds, then I wouldn't be approved for this procedure," I answered.

"Exactly," Dr. Austin said as she further explained using a chart to illustrate the role a healthy BMI plays in fertility treatment versus an unhealthy BMI.

"See here, this is where you want to be to increase chances of success and decrease complications. Since you're only doing retrieval and freezing, your cost is $10,000," Dr. Austin continued.

"Oh, wow... What is that for?" Pam asked in complete shock.

"It is for the check-ups and monitoring during the treatment and the procedure of removing the viable eggs and storing them. The nurse, Nicole will explain the medication and how to get it," she explained.

"Okay, so what about the cost? I was told the clinic could help with the costs because of my cancer diagnosis," I said.

"The clinic has a program for qualified patients that covers 50 percent of the cost. So, all you have to do is pay $5,000 for the procedure and hopefully Nicole can help with more resources. Before you meet with her, let me check and see if the exam room is ready."

Dr. Austin stepped out, which gave me time to check on Pam. In all of my excitement, I noticed Pam's not-so-pleasant expression. I knew she did not understand the costs and procedure, which was totally understandable.

"What's wrong, Pam," I asked.

"Nothin. I'm fine," she said, but I knew she wasn't, but continued, "It doesn't include medication? Well, what does it..."

"Pam, I will explain later. It is okay, I promise," I said in my most reassuring voice.

"I just don't understand why you won't go ahead and start chemo. I am worried about *you*. I want *you* to be okay," she said.

I could tell that she did not want to be there and did not care if I had kids or not. I wasn't offended. I also knew she would not understand. Plus, she had five grandchildren already. I figured she was more focused on my present and I was more focused on my future. I did not blame her for wanting to protect me and keep me safe. We looked at things differently. I appreciated her respecting my decision to see if egg freezing was even possible. And yes, it was possible. I found the other half of the money through the Livestrong Foundation, which also donated most of the medications needed. The remaining meds came from the fertility clinic. I was so thankful for the generosity of others!

I have my team of doctors, plan of treatment, and now I had to prepare for the mastectomy. Since I wanted to freeze my eggs, I had to wait for chemo, which gave me time to remove my breasts, heal, then do the fertility treatment. I was excited to tell Rhonda about my final plans!

It was Sunday, June 25, when Rhonda talked to me about moving out. It was a beautiful day, or so I thought! That date was significant because it was the anniversary of Michael Jackson's death and as a big fan, I always think of him. I figured Pam was tired of me running her all over DC from appointment to appointment, so after church, I decided to give her some alone time. I went upstairs to hang out with Rhonda and watch the BET Awards and drink our favorite red wine.

"Girl, my trip with Pam was so much fun!" I exclaimed, "We did so much in five days!"

"I'm glad y'all had fun. I know you were nervous about going without your sister," she said.

"Yes, I was a bit apprehensive, but since my diagnosis, she has really been trying!" I replied.

We continued to chat about stuff as if she wasn't about to drop a huge bomb on me!

So, after watching a performance on the awards show, during a commercial break, while drinking our favorite wine, Rhonda turns to me and says, "So let's talk about your exit plan."

Still smiling and sipping my wine, I said, "Huh? Exit plan?"

She said, "Yes. I wanted to talk to you about it before my mama died, but so much was going on, I just couldn't find the time when we could sit and just talk." On April 18, her grandmother, who raised her, passed away.

I said, "Okay..."

This is where I am not completely sure of what she said exactly, because my mind went completely *blank*. I was in shock for sure.

She said something about foundation and fire codes, but I can't recall exactly because I was sick and was in complete disbelief of what I was hearing. It was a lot and nothing at the same time.

I interjected, still shocked, "So you are saying I have to move? I mean, you said I could stay as long as I needed to and..."

My heart was in my throat. I was blindsided. I was confused. Once my heart dropped back into my chest, it was racing. I was in total shock at this point.

She continued, "Yeah, but since I replaced the water heater, I just noticed that the house foundation needs to be reinforced and..."

Still somewhat perplexed, I remembered the year before when she told me that after I finished school, I did not have to pay rent until I found a full-time job. I just didn't want her to think I was using her in any way, despite seeing her as family.

"But...I have nowhere to go. Is it money? I can pay you for the time you said I didn't have to. My credit is good. I can get a loan. I mean... I have nowhere to go, so..." I pleaded.

She went on to try to explain, but it was all a blur. I was devastated! All I could think about was going through cancer treatment with nowhere to live!

With tears welling in my eyes and a dry lump in my throat, I asked, "Can I just stay until I am done with chemo? I should be done by the end of the year and can move in January?"

She exclaimed, "Of course! I just wanted you to start thinking about it."

I restated. "I mean, I have nowhere to go and since I am having all this treatment and surgery, I don't know when I can work. I just thought I was safe here. I will figure it out."

"Oh, well I know you have a lot you are trying to schedule and figure out, so yeah, we can talk about it more later," she said.

I said, "Okay. Well let me go make sure Pam is good. I will talk to you later."

I could not mentally process what just occurred. I was floored. It was the longest walk across Rhonda's kitchen, out the backdoor, down the stairs, past our cars, and into my apartment of nearly nine years. My legs were heavy. My heart was broken. I felt like she was throwing me away. I had never felt like that before.

Rhonda was more than my landlord. She was like family, or so I thought. She was security. She was the one person I knew I could count on! She had never left me hanging in *nine years*. I did not know how to begin to process this, so I suppressed it. I knew I could not tell Pam. She does not handle these types of situations well and I knew she would *lose it*! So, I kept this conversation to myself. I was hoping something would change and she would reconsider. Little did I know, it would only get worse.

CHAPTER 7

EVERYTHING MUST CHANGE

―――

For the time being, I had put the conversation with Rhonda behind me. I was already at war with cancer and its impending battles, so I stayed focused on my health. The day before my bilateral mastectomy on July 5, I decided to host a Fourth of July cookout and invite friends to drop by throughout the day. It was a cloudy day, so it wasn't as exciting and fun-filled as I had hoped. Rodger, who had flown in that morning and barbecued for me and my friends. I appreciated everyone who stopped by, but honestly, my emotions were not as erratic as they could have been. I think it was because I realized that the last time, I had sex was the *last time* I would have sex with my original boobs. Dang!

As the time with my "originals" came to an end, I asked Pam to take a picture of them. Not that I would look at the pictures, but I wanted to have something to reference when it was time for reconstruction. Yeah, the joke was on me! I have never looked at those pictures and couldn't use them if I wanted to, as you will read later.

The morning of my surgery, I was nervous, but still kept thinking about the fact that I would never have sex with my boobs again. I had hardly slept the night before, but I was ready for this next step. I was glad my parents were there, but was concerned about them sitting in the waiting room alone. I reached out to friends and sorors to come check on them for me. I later learned that my soror, Constance, brought them lunch, and Ms. Sharon from the Cancer Ministry and my friend from church, Denise, came and sat with them during my surgery.

Dr. Roberts was upbeat and encouraging as usual. I had never undergone surgery before, so when they gave me the calming meds, I was extremely loopy. I joked and demanded that Dr. Roberts give me a Michael Jordan in 1997 with the flu and not a Steph Curry performance. I have no clue how I came up with that comparison, but it was valid. I was extremely delirious, but the comic relief helped with my nerves, as it would for the next five years. The battle of mastectomy was won! Up next, egg freezing; bring it.

I really appreciated Dr. Roberts making my mastectomy outpatient. I had never spent the night in the hospital as a patient, so him releasing me to recover at home was a gift. When I woke up in recovery, Gwen was the first face I saw. She had draped a pink knit blanket across my legs. While on the way home, the first call I asked Pam to make was to Gene. I was still sleepy and could barely talk, but it was important to me that he knew I was okay.

I do not think I fully understood the toll of losing my breasts would have on my self-esteem. I asked Rodger to cover my mirrors and I tried not to look down for about a week. Finally, on Sunday, after church, I took the towels off the mirrors and looked at my chest. It was sunken in and wrinkled, but I was thankful that Clarence was officially Black history.

In the days following my mastectomy, I was overwhelmed with visitors and people checking in. I realized I needed time alone. My parents did all they could and now it was my turn to care for myself, which meant it was time to start fertility treatment.

In the month that followed, I began injecting myself with hormones and going to daily fertility appointments. My first injection was assisted by my sista-friend, Okoye. I was so thankful she was there because I had no clue what I was doing. After about a week, it became routine. What didn't become routine was the daily internal ultrasounds to check the maturity of my eggs. Each day the number changed, which I did not understand at first.

On Friday, August 5, I had four eggs in one ovary and five in the other and they looked like they were almost mature enough to be retrieved. I was looking forward to the retrieval. Those ultrasounds were uncomfortable, but I was also anxious. I was glad I received a text from a friend inviting me to the US/Brazilian Embassy Opening Ceremony party for the Rio Olympics. I had not been out in a while and it would be my first event without my breasts. I was excited to get jazzy!

After a long night of celebrating the Olympics, I had a 7 a.m. appointment to see if I was ready to schedule my egg retrieval. Following my appointment, before heading home, the nurse, Nicole, called me into a private room to discuss what they had seen. I was tired and ready to go home, but I knew I needed to get this scheduled. She explained they had not seen as many mature eggs as they had seen the day before.

"Okay, so do I wait for more to be ready?" I asked.

"Well, no, because if we did that then you would have a menstrual and would have to start this process all over again", she replied.

"Okay, so now what? I mean how many can y'all get?" I asked with increasing concern.

"You still have eggs that can be frozen, just not as many as we expected. We saw two eggs..." she tried to explain.

"Damn! Two? That is it? How did I go from four on one side and five on another to just two?" I exclaimed. My sadness was coming through as anger. I felt like they had given me false hope and now, I did all of this for nothing.

"Unfortunately, yes, it can happen like that. Just because we saw more eggs that looked like they were maturing doesn't mean all of them would get there. All we can do at this point is retrieve what we can or you will have a period, thus forcing you to begin the process again," she explained.

"Nicole, I appreciate all that you have done and your patience with everything. I am not mad at you. I'm mad at the universe, but I know if it is meant for me to have a baby, then God will make a way. Okay, so if I want to freeze the two eggs, what do I do?"

"Oh, you want to freeze your eggs?" she asked as if she was surprised.

"I mean I came all this way. Why not?" I said. It felt like I was convincing myself of the positive side of things. This was what I call a Proverbs 3 moment. I needed to trust in the Lord and not rely on my own understanding.

"You will need to trigger tonight to force ovulation. That is the medication you haven't taken yet. I will talk to the doctor and see how soon you can come in for your procedure."

"Oh okay, I know which one. So, tonight I inject myself and then what?"

Nicole explained the trigger process and that they would call me to schedule retrieval.

Finally, I was able to go home and sleep. I was slowly coming to grips with the fact that I may never have a biological child. Just as I was getting good and sleepy, around 11:30 a.m., I received a call from my brother, Victor. I was annoyed that he called the house phone because I was asleep and had intentionally ignored my cell ringing.

"Hey, Sis. I catch you at a bad time?"

"Well, I was sleep, but what's up? You good?" I responded.

"Oh, my bad. Yeah, yeah, I'm good. Hey, you know daddy is in the hospital?" he said.

I said, "Huh?" At this point, I was sitting up in the bed. He made it seem like it was gossip as opposed to important info about our father.

I was annoyed! "Why wouldn't they want me to know? Why is he in there?"

"He worked the polls on Tuesday for the election and started feeling bad on Wednesday. Me and Shawn told him to make an appointment. I told him he has to be careful being around all those germs," Victor explained.

"But why does he have to be so careful? I don't understand. Has he been sick recently?" I asked.

"Sis, Daddy's cancer came back. He didn't want to worry you with your surgery and everything," Victor said.

"But I thought he...I mean when did he find out?" I said, getting nervous.

"I think he found out in June. He is supposed to start chemo soon. He even had a Big C card party a couple of weeks ago," Victor said.

"Okay, let me call Uncle Gary. I need to know stuff. Gene can't just keep stuff like this from me. Ugh, he irks me sometimes," I said.

"I know, Sis, but he was looking out for you this time," he said.

We hung up and before I called Uncle Gary, I realized something felt different. I didn't know what it was, but this wasn't like before. I mean, this wasn't the first time Gene was in the hospital with pneumonia.

In 2013, about seven months after his stem cell transplant, he developed pneumonia. They said it was his body still healing from the transplant following treatment for myeloma. He spent about a week in the hospital, but he healed. Something didn't sit right, so I called Uncle Gary.

"Hey, Aunt Anita! Is Uncle Gary there?"

"Hey Neosho. Yeah, he is out back putting up the tent. We are getting ready for his birthday party later," she said.

"Oh yeah, that's right! Well, I just wanted to ask him about Gene. Victor just called and said he is in the hospital. Why didn't anyone tell me?"

"Oh, I don't know, but I think Gary and your dad didn't want to worry you since they were talking about releasing him today."

"So, he is okay. I mean, do I need to come home?" I asked.

"I don't think so. They were talking about releasing him last I heard."

"Okay. I feel better. It's been a hard morning for me. I found out they only see two eggs to freeze, so I've been kinda sad all morning and then Victor calls, being all dramatic."

"Oh, I'm sorry to hear that! But, no, you don't have to come home. You just get some rest. I will tell your uncle to call you in a few."

Less than thirty minutes later, Uncle Gary called. Or at least, that is what my phone said.

"Hey Uncle Gary!"

"No, hon, it's Aunt Anita. Gary is on his way to the hospital. He just got a call. Your dad's heart stopped and they keep getting it started, but he keeps going into cardiac arrest."

"Huh? But I thought he was being released today!" I exclaimed.

"So did we, sweetheart. He's gonna call you once he finds out what is going on."

"Okay. Let me call Stacey and see if she can go up there in my place."

Heart racing, I immediately began to pray.

"Lord, don't do this. Don't take him. Not now, Lord."

I called my cousin, Stacey, who was my proxy. She usually checks on Gene for me. We are about three months apart in age. Her dad was Gene's younger brother who passed away in 2001.

In a frantic voice, I said, "Stacey, please go to the hospital. They are saying that Gene keeps coding. I am trying not to freak out!"

"Okay, okay... I'm getting dressed now. I was cutting the grass. I'm getting dressed now," she said.

"Okay, let me call Rodger and ask him to go up there and pray for him," I said.

"Yeah, okay, I will call you as soon as I'm there. I'm almost ready."

We hung up. I called Rodger. I was on the edge of freaking out.

"Rodger, they said Gene keeps coding. Can you please go pray with him?" I said as tears welled in my eyes.

As I told him the specifics of where to go, I heard the beep of call waiting. When I clicked over, I heard sniffles.

"He's gone," Stacey said.

"Huh? Gone..."

"Yea, Uncle Gary just called and said they worked on him for almost forty-five minutes and he kept coding," she said as her voice cracked.

"*Oh, no! No... No, not now... C'mon Gene!*" I yelled. But instead of going into a full ugly cry, I had to pull it together.

With my heart racing, I said, "Okay, I need to call Rodger! He is on his way up there to pray and I have to call my doctors."

It didn't dawn on me until later, but she had just lost one of her surrogate fathers: her Uncle Gene. She was holding it together for me. I called Rodger to let him know not to go up to the hospital to pray.

"Are *you* okay?" he asked as only a parent could.

"I'm mad at him," I said. I could feel the anger welling up in me.

"Well, you can't be like that. The Lord saw fit for him to go. You have to pray about those feelings and accept God's will," he said.

"I know, but dang, why now? He is so hardheaded! Ugh... He would up and die on me like this and on Uncle Gary's birthday... I mean, *who does that? Only Gene!*" I said with a chuckle. "Let me call my doctors and figure out how I am going to get to KC," I said.

"Okay, baby. Me and your mama are praying for you."

I didn't have time to lose it. My emotions were being held together with silly string at this point. I knew I had to get home to KC, but I didn't know if I could fly yet. I had just had a mastectomy a month earlier *and* I needed to trigger, meaning give myself an injection to force ovulation for egg freezing.

I knew nothing would be the same. Honestly, at first, I was too mad to be sad. I could not believe he would up and die *now*. I know that seems selfish, but my father had his own selfish ways and liked to upstage everybody. Well, this was definitely a show-stopping moment! But I had to hold it together and call these doctors. Dr. Roberts, my breast surgeon, was my first call and I immediately asked if it would be okay to fly. I was so grateful that he gave me his cell number.

"Oh, Neosho! I am so sorry to hear that. Well, you're what almost five weeks out. You have healed nicely and aside from that tape issue, you have had no complications, so I don't see any reason why you couldn't fly," Dr. Roberts said.

"Well, I also just found out this morning that I have to trigger ovulation in my fertility treatment so they can take my eggs," I shared.

"Oh goodness and now this..." he said.

"Yes, sir. I am even more sad that they could only get two eggs. I am praying they go in and find more, but two it is."

"Oh, I am sorry, Neosho," he said compassionately.

"It's okay. If I am meant to have children, then I will," I said.

"Well, let me know if there is anything I can do. Make sure you reschedule your appointment as soon as you can," he said.

"Okay. Thanks, Dr. Roberts."

"No problem, sweetheart. My deepest condolences, Neosho."

And now I needed to call Dr. Austin at the fertility clinic. After being told that Dr. Austin was not on-call, I spoke with the doctor who would actually retrieve my eggs. She made sure I was the first one in on Monday morning, so I could catch an evening flight. The fertility clinic was very accommodating and supportive. The weekend nurse immediately offered her condolences and the doctor on-call assured me that Dr. Austin would call the next day, Sunday, and she did.

After getting the all-clear to fly and preparing for my egg retrieval, I made a Facebook post and *boom:* I had a flight and a few more coins so I would not have to worry about money when I got back. Yep, you guessed it, I didn't have a dime!

When I called Uncle Gary to tell him my itinerary, it felt different, as if the air had changed. I knew nothing would be the same.

"Gary, it's Neosho," I could hear Aunt Anita saying, "How are you, sweetheart?"

"I'm okay. Confused. Irritated. Annoyed. Just trying to process it all."

"Yeah, so are we. You are in my prayers and let me know if you need anything. Here is your uncle."

"Hey there? How's it going?" he asked. He is always concerned about others before himself.

"I'm okay. How are you?" I asked with as much concern. "I am so sorry, Uncle Gary! Of course, he would do this on your birthday..." I said. "He is always trying to be the center of attention," I joked.

"Yeah, I know. We were two peas in a pod, ya know..." he replied.

And then he dropped one of those "Gene bombs" on me. After hearing a "Gene bomb," you usually are annoyed and want to say *"oh, hell naw!"*

"Well, I just wanted you to know that your dad wrote that you would handle his services," he said.

"Huh? He wrote it where?" I asked. I mean he never told me anything about his services. All I knew was that he had life insurance.

"I had been talking to him about putting his affairs in order," he said.

This was a lot, but since Rozeta (my sister) was gone, Victor was ill, and Vincent lived in California, I was the obvious choice.

"I figured I had more time to prepare," I explained.

"We all did. Well, he wrote that 'In the event of my passing, my daughter, Neosho, and my brother, Gary will handle all of my arrangements.'"

"That's it?" I exclaimed.

"Pretty much. He goes on to say that he wants to be cremated and Sam Cooke's "A Change is Gonna Come" to be played at his services. I'm gonna head over to the house to get his insurance papers and have all of that here for you," he said.

I knew Uncle Gary would not let me get stressed about the arrangements. I also remember everything he did when my grandmother and auntie passed away. I refused to allow him to shoulder this burden. After speaking with my brothers, we agreed that Uncle Gary should not have to shell out thousands of dollars for *our* father's memorial service. While Uncle Gary is the patriarch of the family, it was not his responsibility to do everything. I am glad we all kept our end of that agreement.

After that final call and last tear of the day, I began to pray and process what had just transpired. I didn't know how to lose a parent. I had three parents for almost thirty of my thirty-six years of life. God was really testing me in every way. First, I get sick. Then, I get evicted. Then, I lose my boobs, and now the Little Old Man up and died on me.

I called Gene the Little Old Man because he was only five foot six and over seventy. It was always a term of endearment. He called me baby girl, roadrunner, and trouble among other pet names. That was our thing.

I figured things couldn't get much worse at this point. Of course, God said, with a smirk, "You think this is the worst? Do you know about Job? Ha... Keep living!" I didn't believe he was laughing *at* my pain, but I did believe he was laughing because instead of trusting him, I was doing what I felt was right.

I am not a pessimist, but this is a lot. Planning my father's memorial service was probably the most difficult time of my life up to that point. I kept asking myself, "how do you lose a parent?"

I began to talk directly to God, "My Lord, does it get easier? Will I ever be able to *just* focus on this war with cancer? This battle has nothing to do with cancer! How do I do this, God? I am not as strong as I think," I said with tears in my eyes.

"You are stronger than you think. I created you in my image, now why would I create you to be weak. Keep fighting, daughter, and remember: this is not your battle, it's mine. Your steps have been ordered and all you have to do is walk."

By the end of the night, I had a plane ticket and the program for Gene's memorial in my head. God will make a way out of no way, won't he! I had a good laugh at myself for thinking it would not work out after God said it would.

I flew to Kansas City the same day I had my eggs frozen: Monday, August 8. I had no idea how painful that procedure would be. Despite my limited mobility, I sat at my Uncle

Gary's kitchen table and planned every part of my father's memorial. In between the family visits, funny stories, and pain, yes, pain, from the squeezing when they hugged me, I wrote and designed the obituary, met with the funeral home, planned the order of service, secured my friends to sing and play the requested song, created a slideshow, and printed the obituary programs. My auntie and uncle drove me where I needed to go and later that week, I could drive myself. I still had discomfort, but I stayed positive and prayed up. I had to constantly remind people not to hug me tight due to my surgery five weeks ago, but people don't listen, especially family. I won't lie, I wanted to punch a couple of them! I know that was the pain causing me to have violent thoughts. That's how painful it was, y'all!

As I was still coming to grips with my biological father's passing, I knew nothing would be the same. No more long calls due to his stutter. No more watching basketball games on Christmas. No more checking in and making sure he is taking care of himself. Then it hit me, Gene not only gifted me left-handedness, my smile, and outgoing personality, he showed me how to fight cancer! The Lil Old Man had done what he was meant to do as a father. His work here was done and mine was just beginning. I am reminded of the classic song, "Everything Must Change." Nothing and no one goes unchanged when you lose a parent.

CHAPTER 8

THE BATTLE OF CHEMO

———

After I returned to DC from memorializing my father, I shared his passing with Rhonda. She had met him when he attended my PhD graduation the previous year. She was shocked and saddened by his passing and offered her condolences. I had been there for her with the passing of both of her grandparents (who raised her), so her sympathies were appreciated, but things had definitely changed between us. I continued to focus on my health and healing, but I could not wrap my mind around how we went from being like family to the stoic way she treated me during chemo. I can't say enough about how we never had a falling out. I believed that by keeping my distance, I maintained some sense of civility and sanity.

My first day of chemo was Tuesday, August 23. It would have been my grandmother's ninety-fourth birthday. I saw that as a good sign. It was a bright and sunny summer day. I wore my Beastie Boys T-shirt and Son of Mars Jordans. I even posted a pic on Facebook to commemorate the day with the caption, "NO....SLEEP... TIL CHEMO!", which is a play on the iconic song, "No Sleep Till Brooklyn" (1987).

I was *ready*! Maaaan, you are never ready for chemo, let me tell ya!

I decided to laugh and joke all day, but I was *not* ready for what came next. After six hours of poison being pumped into my chest, my oncologist told me to eat because I wouldn't have an appetite or energy for the next few days. Plus, I was starving. Since it was Taco Tuesday, I hit up my favorite neighborhood taco spot, which became a chemo tradition since I had infusions every third Tuesday. When I say I was tired, I was *tired.*

I received a call from Rhonda telling me she needed my space for a nanny and that I had to be out by October 1. Yes, you read that right! She wanted me out in *five weeks!* Isn't God funny? He was really testing my faith with that bomb.

In case you've gotten confused by this crazy situation, instead of me moving in January 2017, after treatment, I was being forced to move in five weeks while undergoing chemo. Uh-huh... You read that right! *How Sway?* So, I sucked it up and asked for help. I left my house key in a rock outside my door so people could come and pack up nine years of my life. I mean, of course, I couldn't lift anything due to, um, let me think... *Chemo and a double mastectomy!*

As soon as I pulled up to the restaurant, my phone rang. It was Rhonda. I answered thinking she wanted to see how chemo went because that is what people do: they check on you when they know you are alone and probably drove yourself to chemo. Well, remember how hilariously f-ked up it was to have to move after I finished chemo? Y'all wanna see a dead body? Just wait for it.

"Well, I wanted to talk to you. I just found out Jason has been transferred to Michigan." she began. Jason was the father of her son.

"Oh wow..." I said.

"Yeah, he leaves in a couple of months. This is going to really make childcare difficult," she continued, "So I am going to need to hire a nanny to live in the basement."

Okay, so, instead of there being foundation and fire code issues with the house, she was now asking me to move for a nanny. Ha... Got it! I was almost in disbelief, but at this point I was so hungry and tired and, oh, I was fighting for my life!

"Oh wow... Okay," I said.

"Yeah, so Imma need to you be out by October 1 and—"

I died. In that moment, I died inside. That was a little over a month away, five weeks to be exact. *How Sway?*

"I mean I have nowhere to go. Look, I had my first chemo today, and I am tired and hungry," I said in complete disbelief.

She said, "Oh, I didn't know you had chemo today."

"Yeah, today was my first day, which is why I am trying to eat. My doctor said I won't have an appetite after today," I shared, even though I had told her a few times, including the week after I returned from Kansas City. We had an entire conversation about when chemo would start. But I digressed.

"*And* now I have to find a place to live. I will be out October 1," I said as I ended the conversation.

After that conversation, I felt anxiety and fear toward Rhonda. I was afraid all the time. While I was going through chemo, our interactions were strange and uncomfortable. One of the most uncomfortable moments was when she texted me out of the blue inviting me for breakfast with her and her friend who was dying of Stage Four cancer. I was exhausted, so I declined but it didn't dawn on me until I woke up that she actually wanted me to sit at a table with a woman who was dying of the same disease I am fighting! The invite creeped me out and forced me further into my shell, but hindsight is 20/20. I probably could have shared my feelings with Rhonda, but I was beyond exhausted from the treatment and overly stressed about becoming homeless.

I was tired all the time and slept *a lot* for days at a time. The silver lining is that the immobilizing fatigue did not set in until day four, so the three days after the chemo infusion I made sure I got stuff done, but fear and anxiety were ever present due to me being forced to move in a month. I was confused about life at this point, and then chemo decided to bring one of her *little friends...* Diarrhea!

It is no secret that chemo is a bitch! Not only did she take my hair, but she forced me to use diaper cream. I did not realize how important hair was until I lost it... *Everywhere!* As a result of not having hair down below and suffering from diarrhea, I began to chafe. Goodness, it was brutal and not my idea of a Brazilian wax. I was raw from the wiping and cleaning and having to wear clothes to leave the house. I would just lay naked, spread eagle on the bed. (Sorry, not sorry for that visual.)

It is funny in hindsight, but in those moments, I was miserable. I wore dresses *a lot* out of fear of the friction. I had to be strategic about the "love below," you know. At the recommendation of my friend, Kia, I bought Dr. Boudreaux's Butt Paste, extra strength. That stuff was a godsend! My rash cleared up, but it did nothing for the many trips to the bathroom. I knew my hair would fall out and come back, but what I took for granted was the hair down below. The hair between my legs knew its assignment! I laugh now, but it was hard to get cute and step out when you would exit stage left, weak legged and sweating. Talk about a long drive home and thank God it only happened once, but that one time was during the coveted CBC Week!

The event was one of most anticipated events of the week of Black excellence in DC. As I worked my way through the crowded event space, planned by my late friend Tiffany Johnson, I looked and felt amazing!

"Oh my god... Neosho!" one friend said.

"Hey!" I replied, trying to talk over the music.

"You look good, girl!" she said.

"Thanks..." I said.

"Hey, it's Neosho!" I heard someone say as they grabbed me.

"Oh wait, I can't hug! My chest—" I said nervously.

"Oh yeah, my bad! How are you feeling? I didn't think I would see you out!" It was my friend, who had recently moved to Chicago, but was in town for CBC.

"How are you feeling" was the most redundant question I was asked for the next four years. While I appreciated the concern, it was exhausting to always have to answer. "I'm okay. I mean, today is a good day," became my equally redundant response when asked how I was feeling.

However, in that moment, I really believed it was a good day until chemo brought her *lil friend* out to play. My stomach was never upset, but when you gotta go, nothing—not even death—can stop you! I felt like Kristen Wiig's character, Annie, in the movie, *Bridesmaids*. The entire time people were talking to me, I was clenching my butt cheeks. Much like Annie after eating bad beef at a restaurant, I was trying to play it off, but I was beginning to sweat. I thought, "How can this be happening? Oh no! Not now... Please! Oh god!" As I made my way back through the crowd, nervously saying my goodbyes, I thought, Lord, please get me home. On the longest, most excruciating drive home, I could feel God chuckling.

I bet he was saying, "I gave you free will. You knew this could happen!" I barely, and I mean *barely,* made it home. Ha! Chemo and her little friend did not win, this time! And God said, "You're welcome." He probably had a smirk when he said it too!

He's an on-time God, yes, he is! And then, I started to lose my hair on my head.

CHAPTER 9

THE BATTLE OF CHEMO: INDIA'S JOURNEY

———

My relationship with my hair has always been directly tied to how I thought I showed up in the world: pretty, sexy, militant, and attractive (or unattractive depending on the style or health of my hair). Years ago, a friend affectionately named my afro "India" because he felt that my hair reminded him of, neo-soul artist, India Arie. I loved my afro, so you can imagine how devastating it was to lose it. I mean, technically, it was cancer hair, so I understood it had to go, but like most women, I was still in my feelings. In true Neosho fashion, I laughed and made jokes just to mask the overwhelming emotions that came in September 2016.

I was told my hair would begin coming out after the second round of chemo. Since I had chemo every three weeks and my first treatment was August 23, I figured it would start around September 13. Ha! This book isn't called *God's Got Jokes* for nothin'! My hair started to fall out the week *before* my second treatment, which made me chuckle. The way my life was going, I wasn't surprised.

It was the day after Labor Day. I was getting dressed for an eye doctor appointment. After doing my makeup, I laid down my edges because my hair had so much new growth that my edges were getting fuzzy. After I brushed over my ear, I noticed curls on the toothbrush. I did it again and I saw more curls on the toothbrush. Everyone tells you it will start after the second round, but I thought I was going to be special and it wouldn't come out at all. I figured since I was planning for my hair to come out after the second round, God said, "Lemme show you why you need to stop making plans!"

I tried to go along with God on my hair falling out. Sort of like laughing at my pain. I even told people, "It's cancer hair. I'm not worried. It will grow back healthy and strong!" I used this same mental process when I chose the double mastectomy. I would tell people, "My boobs are killing me. I don't want boobs that are trying to kill me, so they gotta go!" I used to talk to my afro and tell her that she was sick and had to go away for a while. I kind of made peace with losing her and I knew there was a chance of her not coming back. I wore a headband around my edges for like two weeks and kept my twists pulled up.

My biggest issue with India is that she did not grow fast or long. I figured since she didn't grow fast, she wouldn't fall out all at once, however I refused to wake up with a pillow full of hair. That is also why I refused to take my twists out or wash my hair after starting chemo. Nah, you ain't falling out in *my* shower! This is not some dramatic Hollywood movie, but I was also not going to stand in the bathroom mirror and shave it myself. I wanted to be proactive rather than reactive and since it was falling out anyway, why not send India off in style?

There is only one person I trusted to shave my head: my hometown homie who I considered a little brother, Justin. After seeing those extra curls on the toothbrush I use for my edges and feeling my hair tickling my ears, I called Justin. Chile, India was literally falling out!

"What up, Neosho!" he said.

"Hey, Chipmunk!" I started calling Justin "Chipmunk" because he laughs like one. Think about Alvin and the Chipmunks and now think about their laugh. Can you hear it? Yup, that is exactly how he laughs!

"Okay, it's time," I said.

"Time? Time for what?" he said with that laugh.

"My hair. It's falling out. Time to get your flight! I don't want anyone else shaving my head," I said.

"Oh yeah, bet. Have you looked at flights?" he asked.

"No. I mean I can't afford to pay for a flight. Sorry..." I said.

"Aw, okay, well look up some flights and tell me how much they are. I might have a voucher, but I gotta look for it," he said.

I found Justin a flight the last weekend of September. I planned my haircut party, India's Journey, for Sunday, September 25. The timing was perfect! The National Museum of African American History and Culture officially opened that Saturday, September 24 and my homegirl, Amy, invited me as her guest to the opening ceremony. I was honored to attend the historic grand opening! Everyone was there: Oprah, the Obamas, and Will Smith just to name a few. I mean, I could have stopped at Oprah though, right? It was definitely a blessing to be alive and witness history! Since Justin owned a barbershop and worked all day Saturday, he could not leave KC until that evening. It worked out!

That weekend was a bit of a whirlwind. The museum was open to the public and unlike the other Smithsonian museums, you needed a ticket. I surprised Justin with tickets for that Monday, but I had to re-calibrate my mind after the museum opening. I was still wearing headbands and praying about and dreading the huge change that would happen in less than twenty-four hours. First the invite from Amy, then Justin flying in. My village was showing up!

Living so far away from family forced me to reimagine family and to create my own village. Michael was a huge part of my village and offered up his apartment for my haircut party. As I had built solid friendships for the past ten years while living in DC, Michael was one of the most reliable and consistent people in my life. Unfortunately, he was not at the party due to his job as a flight attendant, but like the brother he came to be for me, he made sure I was good before he left on a trip. Like I said, I truly believe in the village concept, and India's Journey affirmed and strengthened that belief.

A small group of close friends came to witness India's journey: sorors, sista-friends, and a few guy friends. They all served a purpose at this time in my life. I asked one of my sorors and guy friends to document India's Journey via video and photographs. I created a playlist for the event and played it on repeat. It was at this time that I discovered the strength that music provided me. I invited several people to witness India's Journey. Only a handful showed up, and it was just who needed to be there.

Once we arrived at India's Journey, my best friend John took charge, which I have learned to appreciate. I realized that this is not the time for me to be the conductor. John made sure everyone made a plate of food and was comfortable. I did introductions and everyone shared how they knew me, what things they had in common, and what they did professionally. It was a good group of amazing people. I felt blessed to have these people in my life.

I was a little nervous about what was about to occur, especially when I saw Justin set up. I mean, he had a whole barbershop spread on the coffee table! He had clippers with all the guards, shears, brushes, and the cape with his barbershop logo on it. Justin came through super official. In that moment, I began to reflect on how long we'd known each other and how we've witnessed each other's growth. I was glad it was him. The head-shaving experience for a breast cancer patient can be ceremonial, therapeutic, and traumatizing.

John and I had planned for him to shave his head in solidarity. His aunt was a breast cancer survivor and he had done that same gesture in her honor as well. I was humbled by that level of support. I have seen videos and movies of friends and family shaving their heads in honor and support of their loved one's hair loss due to chemo. It was rare for Black people and almost unheard of for Black women to shave their heads as an act of solidarity and support. For many Black women, our hair texture doesn't grow as fast as other people. I joked with John about how easy it was for him to shave his head given his military background, but it was the act itself that touched me. Plus, I was nervous *like-a-mug*!

It seemed like Justin shaved John's head in twenty-two seconds! It was as if time sped up and slowed down simultaneously. I mean, goodness, India had held me down for so long: thirty-six years to be exact. She was manageable and somewhat full. I could do almost any style to her and she behaved. The only time she acted up was when I colored her, but that is understandable. Her natural color is almost jet black, so it is hard to color. Other than that, India has treated me right. Once John was bald, I knew it was my time. Justin began cleaning his clippers, shook the hair off the cape, swept the hair from the chair, and looked at me like, *are you coming or nah?* I wanted to be like, "Nah," but my sista-friend, Okoye started playing songs from my playlist and "I Am Not My Hair" began to play. That's when I knew it was real! I sat down for India's journey.

I honestly thought that when he took my hair tie off my hair would just fall to the floor, but nope. My girl India was holding on, y'all! I was pleasantly surprised. When Justin began, I took a deep breath. He used scissors to cut the twists out. Since my hair had grown out a bit from the hair that was twisted in, he just cut to the new growth. After he cut all of the twists out, I realized my hair was almost gone. All that remained was less than half an inch of fuzz, so I braced myself for the buzz. However, Justin put down the scissors and picked up nothing. What he did next, was shocking, slightly traumatic, and low-key hilarious. As I was sitting there, talking and laughing, Justin was not cutting. I touched my head and almost screamed! My head felt like I had balls of fuzz all over. Justin handed me a mirror, and I was shocked at what I saw.

"Oh my God! I look like Fire Marshall Bill!" I yelled, referring to the iconic character from the historic '90s sketch comedy, *In Living Color.*

"Girl, you know you don't—" my soror, Natalie attempted to say.

"Oh wow… Yeah, you…" Okoye reluctantly said with a giggle.

"Oh girl, yes, you look like him!" my sista-friend, Trina, said while cracking up.

Then, Natalie admitted, "Well, yeah I can see it now." Then she joined us all in a good laugh at my spotty head.

"Let me show you sumthin'!" I said the classic line from the character with my upper lip tucked on top of my teeth as we all laughed.

Then, Justin did it. Still, without clippers in his hand, he started. I felt soft touches on the top of my head. I curiously asked, "What are you doin'?"

"I mean, your hair is just sitting there, so I'm picking it," Justin replied.

I have no idea why, but I immediately began thinking of my ancestors. In that moment, when the hair that I spent my entire life growing was leaving me, I was thinking of my ancestors in the fields from sunup to sundown, picking cotton. Weird as hell. I know, right!

"So, you just picking my hair like it's cotton?" I quipped.

"Well, yeah, it's so soft and just sitting there. I don't need scissors or clippers," he said.

"My scalp is itchy and sore. I haven't washed my hair in about a month," I shared.

"Were you worried about your hair falling out quicker if you washed it?" Natalie asked.

"Yes, ma'am. When my hair started falling out around my edges, I knew I couldn't wash it. I definitely thought it would have fallen out faster," I said.

"Yeah, I can see that happening," she said.

Okoye compassionately asked, "You want me to rub your scalp?"

"Yeah, that would be good," Trina said.

"Oh my god, yes, please!" I said.

My head was really dirty and itchy—my goodness! I didn't know if it was itching from the dirt and dandruff or the chemo, but the tenderness was a very different feeling. As Okoye massaged my scalp, I began to cry. She prayed as everyone tried to console me. They probably thought I was crying because I was bald. Well, that was part of it, but I really was crying because I had a fat head and didn't like that roll in the back, which made everyone laugh. John couldn't resist touching the hook and roll in the back of my head. While it was funny, I felt like I now *had* this thing that I found unattractive about men. I know, I know, that is a bit vain, but heck, by this point, I had earned some piece of vanity. My chest was sunken in from having my boobs removed, and my stomach had swelled a bit. I looked like the aliens in the old '80s movie, *Mac and Me*. If you haven't seen it, Google it! Yup, that is what I looked like minus the bug eyes.

While Okoye massaged my head, Justin prepared the clippers for the buzzcut. As the music played and my friends looked on, I felt the buzz on my scalp. This was the first time I felt the buzz of clippers on my head. It felt tingly and gave me a bit of relief. In my head, I began to sing "No Weapon" by gospel singer, Fred Hammond. My spirit recited the scripture, "No weapon formed against me shall prosper" from Isaiah 54:17. I thought, "The weapon of cancer will not prosper, and if it takes me losing my hair to beat it, then so be it. Cancer will not prevail. Cancer will not win."

I was sad to lose my hair, but ready to be done with my cancer hair so that my healthy hair could grow. I was so touched by everyone's compassion for India's journey. While my self-esteem took a hit, I knew that greater was coming.

My bald head was less than a week old when I, along with my friend and mentee, headed to Philly for the Beyoncé concert at Lincoln Financial Field. Not even chemo could keep me from Queen Bey! I cannot believe it rained the entire concert, but it was such an empowering experience. I felt like I had a secret that no one knew, as if I had a superpower that gave me strength to be in the rain bald with a compromised immune system. Oh, and in case you are wondering, I never got sick during chemo. Not even a cold. The most empowering thing about that concert was when she sang, "Survivor!" We were having so much fun singing along, rain and all. The next thing I knew, Allen and Andre were singing directly to me! I felt seen. I wanted everyone to know that I'm a survivor. I refused to look like my situation and was proud to show off. I have always liked that song, even though it is low-key shady as hell, but it resonates so much with my journey. I was making chemo look good, y'all, rain or shine!

The movies really make chemo look like death and dying, which is not true for many of us. I never thought I was going to die during chemo. I started chemo on my grandmother's birthday, Tuesday, August 23, and my final chemo infusion was Tuesday, December 13, my Uncle Junior's birthday. They both had passed away, so I knew they were the angels covering me during this battle. I also knew they had a hand in making sure I looked amazing whenever I left the house, because when either of them stepped out, they made sure they turned heads. My beat face, smile, and faith became my whole armor of survivorship. God gave me laughter that proved to be my therapy. The way I approached this battle of chemo was evidence of my willingness to fight. Chemo tried it, didn't she? Well, she should've tried Jesus and not me!

CHAPTER 10

IT TAKES A VILLAGE

The hours spent in chemotherapy allowed me to reflect on how blessed I was, despite the obvious. While listening to my gospel music and dozing off, I was always at peace. Chemo sleep is almost as good as anesthesia sleep. *Almost.* The sleep helped me reflect and receive the spirit of blessings. I mean technically this was not the first time I had to scramble to find a place to live. It was just the first time I was forced to move, not to mention, while sick.

In 2005, when I traveled to Los Angeles to pay my deposit on a shared apartment, I was flaked on by a potential room-mate and left without a place to stay for the weekend, let alone a place to live when I moved in two weeks. Stephan, one of my KC homies and film critic, was in LA to screen a film. When I reached out about my jacked-up roommate situation, he was more than gracious.

"What up, girl!" he said in his loud, overly articulate voice.

"Hey. You will not believe this, but the girl I was supposed to share an apartment with is nowhere to be found! She won't answer her phone or respond to my emails," I said.

"What? So, what, you need somewhere to stay when you move?" he asked.

"Well, I just found a room to rent so I'm good on when I move, but I don't have a place to stay for the weekend."

"Oh, that's easy! Come stay with me at the Four Seasons in Beverly Hills. I'm here till Sunday. I'm screening *Guess Who* tonight, you can roll to that if you want," he replied. I always loved how he was always on the move! There was never a dull moment with Stephan.

"Cool. I will meet you there! Thanks." I was so relieved and excited.

This is what a village does. When you need a place to lay your head, they make sure you are good, as I have done over the years as well. Your village not only comes when you are flaked on, but also when you are diagnosed with breast cancer. They check on you and help when they can. My natural ability to make connections and maintain friendships has afforded me to know some dope-ass people. The colloquial saying, "My friends are dope!" definitely applies to people I have encountered. When I was diagnosed, I was not prepared for the shifts in so many of those relationships.

I heard several "nos" and a lot of "I can'ts," but I heard even more "what time" and "how much" throughout my journey with breast cancer. I quickly learned that this journey is not for fragile relationships. While many showed up for me in the early months of my diagnosis, the years that followed took its toll on a few relationships. I still get sad about it, but I have made peace with it. Just like the old saying goes, some people are in our lives for a reason, a season, or a lifetime.

There were several friends who held me down for about a year and a half, but when my mental health was suffering and forcing me to delete people from social media, they took it to mean their season in my life was up. That was *absolutely* not the case, but no one asked me why I deleted them. They made assumptions and just disappeared. When I reached out, radio silence. This was when I realized that their seasons were up, and while seasons changed and people came and went, I still had a village.

I have had long periods of silence and continental distance between me and a few people, and yet we always pick up where we left off! It was amazing at how severe of a storm a quality relationship can weather. I noticed myself laughing at the frivolous things that caused people to remove themselves from my life because God was washing away toxic relationships that bore no fruit. I also grew to admire those who didn't have much, but gave me their time, whether it was visiting me in the hospital or helping me move or sitting with me in my bedroom while I slept. I have been immensely blessed, and while I wish I could name each person who paid a bill or sent a meal that list would be a book itself.

Just as the seasons changed, so did my village. God knew who was needed, when they were needed, and how they could help, but He was stingy with the information. He revealed what I needed to know in the moment, so I later understood.

I wasn't prepared for those seasons and all of the changes that came with them like when things fall away in autumn or, in my case, people fell away. In the spring, we see things blossom and new people step in to replace those missing pieces, which became my gentle reminders of God's hand in my situation. We all know how the summer can be hot and sticky. Well, all that heat and humidity caused relationships to melt away. And then there's the winter when I've felt cold and alone. In those winter moments, especially when calls went unanswered or public attempts at hugs were disingenuous, I was crushed.

I always wanted to hold on to people and relationships longer than I needed to. I didn't discern that the season was changing, which could have been attributed to my unmedicated ADHD. When Rhonda said I had to move out in five weeks, I did not realize that a new season had arrived, causing me to hold on to the relationship when I should have let go. I eventually realized this is when I was struggling with homelessness. The season of living in Rhonda's basement was over.

I shared my diagnosis with a colleague and (somewhat) mentor and mentioned having to move in January after chemo. She immediately offered to let me stay with her, which gave me some comfort in knowing I had a place to go. Unfortunately, that comfort was short-lived because the same day I learned I had to move in five weeks, the offer was abruptly rescinded. I was hurt, but not broken.

I remembered a friend offered to let me stay in her extra bedroom that was used for storage. Then, in true comedic fashion, about a week later, she called in tears. She explained that she wouldn't be able to give me a place to stay, but would always be there for me. When she called, I was so tired from chemo. I appreciated her being honest with me. I understood the toll my cancer was having on, not just family, but also friends. I was not surprised that yet another person was rescinding their offer of a place for me to stay. Even now, I chuckle at the thought that I was sick and had nowhere to live!

I prayed and continued to fight, day after day, week after week. I knew someone would come through for me, but God hit me with another tag on this joke of not finding a place to live. After a couple of potential places to live fell through, my friend Michael said, "Chile, come stay with me until you find a place." I thought it was funny that the one person that said they had room for me really didn't, but he made room for me. And that's how I feel about a lot of things now. People will make space for you. Even when they don't have a room, they will make one for you. A real friend is one who walks in, when the rest of the world walks out (Winchell, 2021). Michael was a real one!

Michael said he would sleep on the couch and I could have his room. He knew I slept a lot, which was such a blessing. He had come through for me even before my diagnosis because that was the nature of our friendship. When I met Michael, we became instant friends. I stole him from another friend, as I often do, and we were inseparable from 2010 until his death in 2018. My auntie called Michael my angel because God sent him to me in my time of need. Little did she know, he was one of many who showed up for me throughout treatment, surgeries, and the many times I had to pack up and move.

It took the full five weeks and several friends and sorors to pack up nine years of my life. Keep in mind, while they were packing, I was asleep. I would wake up to prepared meals, a clean space, and even fresh flowers courtesy of Cynthia, a friend I met in 2007 at an Urban League meeting. Due to the limited space, I had to take some boxes to the storage facility to make room for more boxes, but, of course, I could not lift anything, so I called Don and Bryce.

I met Don about a year after I moved to DC, around 2007, when his party promotion group would host happy hours and events around town. I met Bryce through a consulting job with my friend. Since we were all Howard alums and lived in the same neighborhood, it was nice to know I could call on them for help with those boxes. They loaded Don's truck and took a bunch of boxes to the storage unit for me. This was not the first nor last time these two gentlemen came to my aid, especially Don. From sending me money to having meals delivered, Don was a constant support in my cancer journey.

When I had no energy to cook, Don's business partners, also friends of mine, came through with about two weeks' worth of catered meals, which was during one of the most difficult periods of my journey. My Lord, where would I be without my village!

From day one, my village showed up and showed out! I have always had various circles of friends, friends I stole from other friends, Sorors, ministry friends, and other amazing people I have met over years who came through when least expected it. Throughout this journey I have discovered how valuable relationships can be when the life you thought you had was crumbling around you. I leaned on the shield, tapped into my faith, and opened myself up to receiving more help than ever before.

Denise, my friend from church, was the first call I made after I received the unofficial diagnosis. She also prayed with me before my dissertation defense and biopsy. She was the one who encouraged me to testify at a Young Adult Ministry service, which brought on a season of growth in my spiritual village. Through my young adult and cancer ministries, God provided amazing prayer warriors, moving help and a handyman on several occasions, hospital visits, and prayers. While many of them were in my village for only a season, I have grown to appreciate what they brought into my life during that time.

At the time of my diagnosis, I had been a member of Delta Sigma Theta for seventeen years, nearly half of my life. Being a part of a sisterhood afforded me so many people to reach out to for guidance and help. I decided to send my three line sisters and three undergrad chapter sorors my conference call number to disclose my diagnosis to all six of them at the same time. Since many of them are in the medical field, I hoped they would give me some insight into what I was about to go through.

Throughout my treatment, my sorors were extremely supportive, and then my mental health issues caused a misunderstanding and all of that changed. I wished I could have approached things differently, but I cannot apologize for protecting my peace. What I found was comfort in the women I pledged with. My line sisters never gave up on maintaining some type of relationship with me. It was also during this journey I realized many of their frustrations with me for the past seventeen years stemmed from my undiagnosed ADHD. While I am sad sorors I've known since I was nineteen were no longer an active presence in my life, they will always be my sisters. The bond of sisterhood in Delta is not limited to college.

My Washington, DC Alumnae Chapter (WDCAC) sorors supported me in ways I could not imagine. I had no idea that asking for prayers before my mastectomy would expand my village as it did. Since I had moved a couple of times before settling down in DC in 2006, I had not been active in a Delta chapter until I joined WDCAC in 2011. Sorors from WDCAC helped pack up my apartment, sent me gifts and cards (I love cards!), bought me meals, and visited me when I needed the company.

All of my Delta sorors blessed my spirit throughout my cancer journey, but bonding with a fellow survivor and daughter of a survivor were special. After the biopsy to confirm my breast cancer, I visited my WDCAC chapter soror and breast cancer survivor, Dr. Netta. She was an ear when I needed to vent and a resource when I was confused about the process. She also came to a few appointments and gave me rides to post-op appointments. She and Soror Jessica were unexpected friendships.

Soror Jessica was a constant presence. From rides to the airport to meal drop-offs, she was also a village navigator. She would even relay messages from other sorors who just wanted to check on me and made sure I had what I needed. If I needed anything, she was a call away. Her mother was a survivor, so she was all too familiar with the medical side of my journey. My Delta village was more than I could have imagined!

When Dr. Patel said I needed three things to beat cancer, support was one of them. The unexpected support of new friends was humbling. Remember, I steal friends from other friends. In addition to stealing Michael from another friend, I stole Monica from my best friend, Anthony. I had just defended my dissertation the Monday before traveling to Milwaukee for his wedding. It was my first event as Dr. Ponder, so I was excited and ready for a trip without having to write anything for school!

Well, the night before my arrival, while watching McDreamy die on Grey's Anatomy, Anthony called to tell me he couldn't pick me up from the airport because his groomsmen surprised him with a trip to Chicago. He knew he wouldn't be in no condition to pick me up at 8:30 a.m., but told me his homegirl was flying in from New York around the same time and was renting a car. Anthony and Monica became platonic friends at a Black Ski Weekend event.

He assured me that Monica was good peoples and would get me to the hotel safe and sound. Yup, I was annoyed that I wouldn't get to hang with my homie before he tied the knot, but I understood.

My goodness, Monica and I literally became instant friends! Neither of us had ever been to Milwaukee and she didn't know a soul at that wedding except the groom and heck, I only knew a few people due to me knowing Anthony from college and him marrying a Delta.

Monica and I were connected by happenstance just one year before my diagnosis and remained a staple in each other's lives. Who knew that over the next twelve months, I would graduate, Monica would move to the DC, Maryland, Virginia area (DMV), and I would be diagnosed with breast cancer? Well, God clearly knew. He ain't slick! In addition to Monica being a woman of God, she was the daughter of a breast cancer survivor, a new doctoral student, and just a really dope chick.

God saw further than we did, 'cause despite her living an hour away, having a demanding job, and writing a dissertation, Monica was present for every step of my journey. She bought boxes and helped me pack, sent money to help with bills, and visited me in the hospital, but the most amazing thing Monica did was treating me to a get-away before chemo. The day after returning to DC from Gene's memorial in Kansas City, I shared with her how bummed I was that I couldn't take a pre-chemo trip because I used funds to cover expenses for the memorial. I knew I would be reimbursed by the life insurance, but by then, I would be in the throes of chemo. After listening to me for a few minutes, without giving it a second thought she invited me to Dallas in three days!

"Girl, come to Dallas. I already have a suite at the Sheraton and I can get your plane ticket."

"Huh? Come to Dallas? What is going on in Dallas?" I asked.

"Chile, nothing really. I have to meet with my advisor. Remember when I told you I'm in an online program but we have to meet four times a year in different parts of the country? Well, this time we are meeting in Dallas. My homegirl, Kesha, is meeting me there too," she explained.

"Oh, wow! That is a lot, girl. I don't want to impose on y'all's trip!" I exclaimed.

"Honey, please! Kesha wants to get away for a few days. She works in law enforcement and needs a couple of days away. Imma be in meetings during the day. Y'all can hang out! She's cool."

"Oh..." I said, feeling impressed, humbled, and kinda confused.

"Okay, I am getting your flight. You fly Southwest, right?" she said in her Type A way.

"Yup..." I replied.

"Okay, when do you wanna leave? We get in tomorrow night. Just let me know when you want to get there and return to DC and I got you."

I flew to Dallas that following Wednesday and had the most restful, fulfilling time! Kesha and I hung out during the day then linked up with Monica at night. I got to visit Anthony and his wife and my cousin, Eric, and his wife, but the highlights of the trip were my tour of AT&T Stadium where my beloved Dallas Cowboys played and The Sixth Floor Museum at Dealey Plaza where President Kennedy was assassinated. That trip was such an amazing gift! I had hoped to take a trip before chemo, but I thought New York or Philly. My sista-friend, Monica was definitely a good "steal" and an important part of my village!

Whether it was a one-year friendship by happenstance or a ten-year friendship built over time, my village always knew the assignment. One of the most amazingly, phenomenal women I had ever met was Tiffany Johnson, who I loving referred to as my own Olivia Pope. She was a boss chick's boss who owned a successful consulting company. Tiffany was like a big sister to me and when I reached out about financial assistance during chemo, she created a consulting job for me. Yes, *created* a job so that I could pay my bills for the month. Throughout my treatment, she would come through when no one else could, whether it was a ride to chemo or sage professional advice. She was a straight shooter! Her pep talks were motivational monologues or culturally speaking "reads" that left me empowered and in tears.

To have Tiffany in my village provided me with so much wisdom and access. As I said, Tiffany was the boss of a boss chick. Her connections were deep and in September 2017, because of Tiffany's connections, I was afforded the opportunity to share my breast cancer story in a BET (Black Entertainment Television) campaign that would air the following October for Breast Cancer Awareness Month.

During the filming, the producer asked me about my village and before I could respond, I went into a full-on ugly cry. When I say ugly, I mean, U-G-L-Y YOU AIN'T GOT NO ALIBI, kind of ugly! I mean, the thought of those who had been supporting me for the previous year and a half hit me like a ton of bricks. I had not thought about it up until this point, because when you are *in it* you don't see the larger impact people are having on your life. Through my village, I was entertained by God's irony, covered by the blood of Jesus, and comforted by the Holy Spirit.

As I reflect on my village and how they have supported me, I see why God removed people in those winter seasons, added people in those springtime moments, and made sure those sticky summer situations did not disrupt my faith. God be knowin'! My ability to connect with people easily has not changed. I have found virtual villages as well. I am active in several Facebook support groups and they have blessed me immensely. After so many seasons changed, I practiced more discernment, mourning past relationships less and less. I am definitely a ride or die friend, but have learned to appreciate the seasonal friends, value the reasons for seasons, and recognize the lifers. Whether planned or unplanned, provoked or not, in the words of the prophetess, our good sis Tabitha Brown, "When things leave naturally, *let 'em go* (Brown, 2021)."

CHAPTER 11

WHEN (WO)MAN PLANS, GOD LAUGHS

———

If you think chemo was difficult, just think of how it was while moving! If you think going through chemo and moving was difficult, then try going through chemo, having to move, and then having to move *again!* I swear my battles were trying to one-up each other with these moves from house to house. It was daunting and this was just the beginning!

I was thankful for my friend, Michael, giving up his bed and letting me stay with him for a month and a half while I recovered from the blindsided eviction, but I was desperate to find a more accommodating space. After months of begging on Facebook, one of my sorors told me about a friend of a friend who had an extra room with a bathroom who was open to meeting me to see if she wanted to rent it to me. I met with the woman. I was glad she was told about my situation prior to meeting me, so she wouldn't be surprised by my appearance or condition. Ms. Jackie was an older Black woman who was very open to helping me. We agreed that

I would stay with her for only $500 per month for about the next six months while I finished chemo and radiation. I figured I would start interviewing during radiation, then get a job and move by the end of spring, hence the title of this chapter. I have learned not to plan so much and focus on the moment.

Again I was moving and *again* my village came through for me! With Michael letting me keep some stuff at his place, I asked a few girlfriends to help me move into Ms. Jackie's house. Now, this house should really be a historical landmark or something because when you walk through it, it is like walking through a museum. Art was displayed from floor to ceiling and everywhere in between. It was almost overwhelming, but then you realize that this woman not only displays art, she also preserves history. It was truly a beautiful sight to see, unless you lived in it.

By Thanksgiving, I had settled into my new place and mourned the results of the 2016 presidential election. I was looking forward to my parents and nephews visiting me for the holiday. I had a fun-filled weekend planned that included bowling, game night, church, and a trip to the "Blacksonian." My family visiting for Thanksgiving was the boost I needed! It made me even more excited for Christmas, especially since I did not go home the previous year.

My final round of chemo was Tuesday, December 13: what would have been my late uncle's birthday. I was excited to ring the bell, but unfortunately, my oncologist did not have one. Most cancer centers have an actual bell for patients to ring when chemo has ended. It seemed to be somewhat ceremonial, but no bell for me. Since I still had eight months of Herceptin, due to my HER2+ status, maybe Dr. Patel didn't see my treatment as being done. I asked the nurse to take pictures and I happily posted on social media. I was unbothered about not ringing the bell and *onest again* the village came through. My homegirl celebrated with me over tacos! Then, a week later, bundled and masked up, I was wheeled onto a flight to KC. I came to appreciate the wheelchair service at the airport.

Since I missed Christmas with my family in 2015, I had so many people to see and things to do. But... this book isn't titled, *God's Got Jokes* for nothin'! Just when I thought I was done with chemo, her li'l friend diarrhea decided to visit and refused to leave. I spent 90 percent of Christmas Day either sleep or running to the bathroom. How am I gon' have diarrhea on Jesus' birthday! I was like, *"Really, God? Really?"*. Thankfully, I was feeling better by the new year and gearing up for radiation and the job hunt. And then the Lord said, "More jokes to come..."

The weeks between chemo and the start of radiation were quite eventful. In early January 2017, I was interviewed about my cancer journey by a local CBS reporter who came across my GoFundMe page. I was interviewed about how the Affordable Care Act, better known as "Obamacare," saved my life by helping me to afford health care coverage. I shared how I had just gotten the coverage before discovering the lump and that due to my lack of income, I did not pay for my cancer treatment and doctor appointments. Obamacare worked and I was living proof!

Shortly after the interview, I began radiation and was really focused on finding a job. I was told I would undergo twenty-five rounds of radiation and honestly, I didn't know what that meant. But, like with everything on my journey, I was ready to fight. I had treatment Monday through Friday, with every other day being targeted radiation therapy.

The room was soooo cold! For the targeted therapy they put this thick plasticky, silicone-like thing over the radiated area every other day. I specifically asked what it was for and the tech told me it was to direct the radiation to the area where the cancer was found. I thought that was interesting but did not give it much thought past that question. I was staying the course, working my plan, and then an unexpected call gave me some much-needed excitement.

A couple of weeks after beginning radiation, I was out to brunch with my friend, Monica, when I received a call from CNN. Naturally, I thought it was a joke, but after a nice little laugh with the producer, she confirmed that she was a producer at CNN. She called about that Obamacare article that was written about me and invited me to participate in a CNN Town Hall about the Affordable Care Act. Still in disbelief, I asked her a few questions about the event and confirmed my participation, including if Anderson Cooper would be moderating. He is my husband in my head!

Of course, after hanging up, I immediately, said "Look at God!"

"What? What was that about?" Monica asked.

"Girl, that was CNN! Oh my god, I hope I see my boo, Anderson!" I said.

"You do love you some Anderson!" she said with a laugh, "CNN, though? They want you to be on CNN? Really?"

"Yes, girl! I cannot believe it!"

"How did they know to call you? Where did they get your info?" she asked. I forgot Monica is in law enforcement! Ha!

"Good question! I mean she said she found me through that story the reporter did. Remember?"

"Oh yeah! Oh okay, so maybe they found your number through your GoFundMe," she said.

"Maybe. It's on Tuesday, February 7. You gon' come with me?"

"Oh okay, I can go with you," she said.

In case you don't remember, I met Monica in an airport in April 2015. We have been friends ever since! Every time she shows up for me, all I can say is, "Thank you, Lord, for my friend!" Cue the *Golden Girls* theme song! After processing what had occurred, I called to ask John to come as well. I couldn't go on CNN without my best friend!

Even though I was local, they still got me a hotel room for the night, treated us to dinner, and made sure we were accommodated the entire evening. I hate that John couldn't make dinner, but Monica did and she stayed with me in the hotel. At dinner, the producer broke the news that Anderson Cooper would not be moderating the town hall. I was a little bummed, but I got the opportunity to participate in a discussion about the Obamacare.

Jake Tapper and Dana Bash moderated, with Senators Bernie Sanders and Ted Cruz as guests. The town hall format allowed citizens to ask the Senators questions about Obamacare and how the law has affected them. This was during a time when the current administration was trying to gut the law that the Obama Administration enacted, thus making it impossible for people like me with pre-existing conditions to receive cancer surgeries and treatment covered by insurance. I was ready for this, especially after crying my eyes out on election night for fear I would lose my health care.

When Hillary Clinton lost the election, her opponent vowed the repeal *my* healthcare. Participation in this town hall was essential not only to my health, but so many others with pre-existing conditions. I asked Senator Cruz a question that never got answered, but I didn't expect a straight answer. Chile, he even tried to lump me into the same category as his mama because she was a survivor. Um, no, sir, we are *not* the same, but I was seen and heard!

This experience reminded me of that song I didn't completely agree with, "I Am Not My Hair." As you know, I hated losing my hair. I usually wore hats, which I looked good in, so my CNN debut would be the perfect occasion to rock my favorite H&M fedora until the producer said my face would be blacked out due to the lights. Well, there goes that *plan*, I thought, then I saw it as a sign that the world needed to see me in my bald glory! I felt like India Arie's lyrics were on full display that night. Yes, breast cancer took away my crown and glory, but that verse goes on say so much more. I promised God that if I survived this, I would enjoy every day of my life. I never thought that I would actually be on national television, but since India Arie was speaking to me, she must have noticed how my diamond eyes were sparkling during that CNN Town Hall. Oh, and for the first time my bald head was like a full moon shining!

I was never comfortable with my bald head, but when I asked Senator Cruz about the Affordable Care Act, I felt proud to be a cancer patient. I didn't need a hat, scarf, or hair, because my face was beat and my eyes were sparkling. I even made sure everyone knew it was Black History Month by rocking the original "Because of Them We Can" t-shirt with my faux leather sleeved blazer. Y'all couldn't tell me nothin, chile! I needed that boost of confidence. Since chemo ended in December, I had been having monster hot flashes to the point that I sweated through my sheets causing me to constantly kick through the night. I was so restless and kicked so much that I wore a hole in my sheets. So, yes, my mind needed to unwind and my self-esteem needed a little boost.

A week after my CNN debut, on February 13th, I started to notice the radiated skin peeling in my armpit. This was before my thirteenth radiation treatment. My skin had already turned extremely dark, but that was normal. When I brought it to the tech's attention, she said she would tell the doctor, but assured me it was normal. Unfortunately, my radiology oncologist was only at that hospital one day a week, so I had to wait a few days to show her in person. When she finally saw it, she asked if I'd been using Aquaphor. No one had told me about it until that day, which was a few days after I noticed the peeling. The tech and nurse gave me some sample sized Aquaphor and told me I had to get more. I was surprised that no one told me this before.

By the third week of February, I was in excruciating pain! Since my radiology oncologist was only there once a week, she was always told secondhand about my condition by a nurse or the tech. The Friday before Presidents Day, I started noticing bumps at the bottom of the dark, radiated area. I also noticed the patch in my armpit had pink spots. Unfortunately, my radiology oncologist was not there that day. I asked if there was anyone who could look at it. Another radiologist looked at and prescribed me pain meds, but no one told me that due to the opioid crisis, I wouldn't be able to get it filled in DC unless I waited the three to four hours at the hospital. The only pharmacy I could find close enough to

DC but not in it was just over the Maryland state line. It was a nightmare because the doctor prescribed too many pills and I had to get a new prescription, thus forcing me to wait until the following week to get pain meds. I really hope you are following 'cause this was when my plans were completely thwarted and took a turn for the worse.

The pain persisted with no reprieve in sight. During President's Day weekend, a friend offered to bring me some pain meds. I know, I know, it is not safe to take meds from other people. I tell people that all the time, but this was a pain like I'd never felt before! They brought me two of the exact same meds I was prescribed. I can't stress enough how much relief those pills brought me! I have to admit, there was still some occasional burning but I could function normally, which was what I prayed for. Though short-lived, I was grateful for the relief.

When you are in unbearable pain, it affects with your mental health. Yes, the pills from my friend helped, but, like I said, it was very short-lived. I figured during that short amount of time I could continue to look for a job. I was working my plan! I found a position with an organization that I was interested in, but I wanted to run it by someone who was familiar with the organization. Mental stability and physical health are essential when communicating with others, especially when they may not know your present state. However *(comma)* the situation went left for no reason.

I sent a text to someone I considered a friend asking about the position and I kept getting short responses. Desperate to find employment, I asked further questions about the place and the hiring manager. What happened next was a complete shock and left me speechless.

She replied and told me that I wouldn't be a good fit and, in so many words, me texting her on a Saturday is an example of why. Then she said if I wanted to discuss further, she would call me on Monday. Still in shock, I just said, "Wow, okay." She seemed irritated by me asking as if she didn't know I had been sick and struggling. I mean she had never worked with me, so how would she know I wouldn't be a good fit? I was asking about the organization, not her opinion of me. My mind began to spiral, and the pain had kicked back in. I was confused, hurt, and devastated that someone I had known socially for years saw me as not being a good fit for an organization. It felt like she was saying "the organization is great, but you're not." My soul was crushed! I went to bed brokenhearted and in persistent pain.

When Monday, Presidents' Day, came, I was having thoughts of harming myself. I cannot recall ever having these feelings before. Was it the pain that caused these thoughts? Was it out of frustration of not working that I began asking myself questions?

The next few days were hard. I had to walk around the house without a shirt and my left hand resting on my head because the bumps had become extremely painful. I was sad, depressed, and in pain: three emotions no one wants to endure while dealing with the effects of cancer. I was supposed to be almost done with cancer. I had plans!

God chimed in and asked, "Plans? Who made them?"

"I did," I replied.

"And therein lies the problem," the Holy Spirit quipped.

"But I thought I just had to—" I attempted to explain.

"Stop, just stop. You just have to be obedient and heal," God said.

"And stop making plans! We got you," Jesus chimed in.

I just wanted life to be over at this point. I began to pray and really think about the person that sparked all of these feelings out of nowhere and made peace with the fact that she wasn't the best person to talk to about employment. It made me chuckle a bit! Maybe *she* was the problem. I prayed for those feelings of harming myself, depression, and self-deprivation to go away. While it sounds simple, it is not simply done. It took some difficult days and nights to come to terms with everything I was feeling. But God...

The impetus for those feelings of self-harm was the pain. I thought, *Make it make sense!* Why are these bumps hurting so much? Why isn't the Aquaphor working? Due to the bumps and pain, my radiology oncologist paused my radiation, which told me everything I had planned would be pushed back. The bumps were not bumps at all! Come to find out, they were blisters, hence the burning and pain! Now my thought was, *What in the entire f**k? The next battle in Neosho's war with cancer is a radiation burn! Make it make sense! How Sway?* I had plans! I did not want to wait, thus prolonging treatment. I was supposed to live at Ms. Jackie's until after treatment, six months at the most. I was supposed to be interviewing for jobs. I was supposed to be planning my reconstruction.

While I never believed that God caused my burn, I did have several internal battles with my situation. Clearly, at this point, I had not accepted God's hand in my cancer journey. While I had strong faith, I had already been dealing with hot flashes, self-doubt, and thoughts of suicide and now my radiation was causing issues. *Really, God? Really!* I was mad. No, I was pissed! I began to wonder if I had done something to deserve this. Since then, I realize that it wasn't what I did, it's what I didn't do. I did not trust God. Instead of trusting Him, I was making plans.

CHAPTER 12

AND SO IT BEGINS: TRAUMA AND LOSS

———

Trauma comes in various forms. It was traumatic to be forced to move, and it was traumatic to be removed from my former landlord's life. Listen, I had whole ass nightmares about her! Trauma. In 2008, my oldest sister, Rozeta, was murdered by her husband, who is now in jail. I have experienced different levels of trauma, but none of my previous life experiences would have prepared me for what was coming: a severe radiation burn. Doctors and nurses have told me to my face they had never seen a burn that severe. It was at that point that I began to worry.

Please prepare yourselves for what you are about to read because I cannot mince my words or gloss over the descriptions of the burn's stages. Due to the pain and severity of the burn, my radiology oncologist stopped my radiation treatments. I had twenty-one of twenty-five rounds of intense radiation that involved targeted therapy. I pointed out my skin peeling and pain between treatments thirteen and sixteen. So, for a whole-ass week, rounds seventeen to twenty-one, I kept receiving the same dosage of radiation, while only seeing the doctor on Fridays, because, remember, that is the only day she is in the hospital. As a patient, this was extremely frustrating! I felt neglected at times. I was relieved when she said to stop treatments, but I continued to go to the office regularly.

You might be wondering why I had to go to the radiology oncologist if she stopped radiotherapy. And that's a great question! As I sit here writing this, I can only muster an annoyed smirk. This was another moment in time where all I could think was, "Really?" The timeline is uncanny to read and visuals are devastating to see, but to live it was unimaginable. Please read all that comes next carefully because the dates are mind-boggling.

I took pictures almost every day, beginning with the day I noticed the peeling in my armpit, February 13. I am so thankful I did, because people would never believe me if I didn't have receipts. There we were, trying to process this new development and get it treated.

The radiology tech and nurse told me to put Aquaphor and aloe on the burn, when there was no change, I had to have the burn debrided. This is when I realized that this is not normal. Every other day, I had to have my burn debrided and chest wrapped. Yes, every other day! This made life very difficult. As you will learn throughout this book, I name everything! If I had to name this burn it would be Vin Diesel 'cause this thang developed fast and furious! Once the burn spread, which took less than a month, it covered my entire radiated area.

More evidence of the irony and hilarity of my situation was that my former landlord was a certified wound care specialist, so I knew there were medical professionals who dealt with wounds. When the blisters became an actual burn and expanded up my chest and then the pink spots in my armpit became more and more red and also spread, I immediately asked the radiology oncologist, Dr. Ro, if I could see a wound care specialist. My request was brushed aside and since she was the doctor, I trusted her.

The date and time stamps on the pictures do not lie, and they create an uncanny timeline! I explain the development of my burn in descriptions of things people are familiar with or have at least seen.

The radiated area of my chest started looking like a dark shadow by the date of my CNN appearance on February 7. No pain or concerns. At this point, I was thinking everything was fine. But a week later, February 13, I started to notice my skin peeling in my armpit.

By February 17, painful bumps developed and I was told to use Aquaphor and aloe. The bumps looked like a disease, like an STD. They kept radiating me until February 24. During this time, the entire dark shadow became the huge, black scab.

By February 24, my burn was on full display! The black scab began to look like a brisket. It took an entire week for my doctor to say, "Okay, let's stop the treatment".

I thought, "You don't say!"

By February 27, just three days later, the area that originally started peeling on February 13 had begun to cry tears of blood. It looked like a medium rare smoked brisket, charred on the outside, but not cooked inside. Sorry, but not sorry for the visual. I gave a disclaimer just so no one would stop reading at this point. Stopping the treatment was probably best. Ya think?

After treatment was halted, I still had to go to the radiology oncology treatment office to have the brisket debrided. My chest had to be shellacked with a burn cream called Silvadene, then a layer of xeroform gauze was laid on top of the Silvadene. Then, the nursing assistant would wrap my chest with thick, sterile gauze. Oh, and I was not on pain meds when this started. Dr. Ro would prescribe me ten pills at a time and since she was only there one day a week, it was like hell getting meds! I even went to her other office in Maryland to pick up a prescription.

The debriding felt like torture, if you want to know the truth. I think it was the debriding that prompted my doctor to prescribe me a thirty-day supply of oxycodone. I never, I repeat, *never* became dependent on any of the meds I was prescribed. As you continue to read, some of you will begin to wonder and I wanted to be upfront about that. I do understand the restrictions around prescribing opioids, and I am thankful addiction isn't a genetic trait for me.

Vin continued to change and attempt to heal. It was a horrible sight!

March 1 was when the brisket became a salmon and then the next day, March 2, I noticed my hair was growing! How did I miss this? I felt like a parent missing their child taking their first steps. I had missed this big event because of this damn burn!

From March 2 to 8, Vin evolved from a salmon to a raw steak. I continued to ask for a wound care specialist, and my requests were continually dismissed. The doctor seemed to act as if I was getting the same care in the radiation treatment center. There was so much going on that I nearly forgot about the National Holiday: my birthday.

I had begun chronicling my journey on Caring Bridge shortly after my diagnosis and below is my entry for my birthdate:

"On March 9, 2017, I turned 37. I have NO IDEA what that means. I thanked God for another year, but still teared up thinking about the year that led to me turning 37. A year ago, I thought I was spending my thirty-seventh bday in Cuba. Instead of me waking up, 37, in Cuba, I woke up a cancer survivor...so I immediately thanked God! I had to make peace with my current life, so I decided my theme for 2017 is #FOR-WARD." (Ponder, 2017)

March 10 was the first day I noticed Vin attempting to heal. It started to look like pickle loaf! Hilarious, 'cause my grandmother loved pickle loaf, so that was my immediate thought. There was a light at the end of the tunnel!

The pickle loaf lasted the rest of the month, and then I noticed it really healing. I mean skin pigmentation and all. It was interesting to see it heal from the outside in, but it was healing slow as a mug! Upon the realization that the burn would take a while to heal, Ms. Jackie allowed me to stay until the burn healed. I was grateful.

I felt like I was living in an alternate universe. The next few months included me creating a bandage bag and carrying it everywhere. The radiology oncologist, Dr. Ro, told me I no longer needed to have my bandage changed in the treatment center, so I had to start doing my own wound care. I mean, I cannot believe she ignored my many requests and in hindsight, I can't believe I didn't advocate harder or just replace her.

While I am dealing with all of this, my landlord, Ms. Jackie, did not turn the air conditioning on in June. I had a window unit in my room but going to the bathroom or even getting water was a challenge due to me having to walk around without a shirt to let my burn breathe between bandages.

More than three months after my last wound treatment in the radiotherapy office, on Thursday, June 15, I planned to make tacos with my soror and her fiancée, Candace and Tye, who basically kept me fed the entire time I lived with Ms. Jackie. Since Ms. Jackie is vegan, I never cooked in the kitchen. I warmed up food, but was never comfortable preparing a full meal. I ate out a lot, so when Candace suggested that we have a taco night, I was excited. I made a video to update my family and friends on my progress the night before and I felt okay, besides the pain. I woke up that Thursday in a cold sweat and chills. I got dressed to head to the store to get stuff for the taco night, but as I began to drive, I started feeling jittery. I called Candace.

"Hey Neosho!"

"Hey. I'm on my way to the store, but I got a late start today," I said, still feeling lethargic and cold.

"Well, how are you feeling? You don't sound too good," she said with a concerned tone.

"I woke up cold and sweaty. I don't feel too hot, but I probably need to eat something," I said.

"Girl, do not go to the store, go to the hospital! Go now and I will meet you there!" she ordered.

"Okay, I am going to the hospital near you," I said.

Her forcing me to go to the hospital gave me some relief. I guess I didn't know if what I was feeling was of concern. I had been going through so much during this time, that I had not paid close enough attention.

I was immediately admitted to the hospital with cellulitis, an infection in my chest wall, and a 103-degree temperature. I learned cellulitis developed due to my burn not healing and probably the heat in the house I lived in. This experience was beyond traumatic! I had never spent the night in a hospital as a patient before now. I was glad Candace stayed with me until they put me into a room. They had me on heavy antibiotics to try to prevent sepsis from setting in. When I heard the word sepsis, I feared for my life. The next day, Friday, my temp went down, but not enough. They continued to watch me closely in case my temperature spiked.

It was during this hospital stay that I began to think I was not going to make it out. I couldn't help but think about Gene and how he went into the hospital and never came out due to sepsis. In addition to my morbid thoughts, I was still in severe pain due to the burn. Unfortunately, pain meds were not always available during my hospitalization. My pain got so unbearable that I thought it was my time. I cried out to God.

"Jesus, help me! Please take the pain away! Lord, I am not ready to leave," I cried. My cries were tear-filled and desperate. It was nighttime, visiting hours were over, and I was alone with my pain. My heart was racing and my mind was all over the place. Finally, I got a response.

"Did you hear my sandals come down the hallway?" he asked.

"No, sir," I said with tears still streaming down my face.

"Then turn over, keep watching Grey's Anatomy and keep fighting," he said.

I was obedient. I rolled over and continued to watch my favorite show on my laptop, still sobbing from the pain. He didn't have to check me like that though, did he? Yes, He did.

I was released on Monday, June 19, that day was met with so many issues and obstacles. I asked again to see a wound care specialist. The nurses explained I had been discharged by the doctor. I explained I was still in a lot of pain and I would like for a wound care specialist to see my burn. When the wound care person came, they suggested the nurse put Manuka honey on my burn. Well, they did exactly that!

The way that honey seared into my burn as if I was being cattle-prodded had me screaming in pain. My breast navigator, Gwen, stopped by and could hear my cries down the hall. There are *no words* that can describe how debilitating the pain was! I begged the nurses to help me and they just stood there. It was crazy! Gwen called my breast surgeon, Dr. Roberts, who asked if they had wet the honey before putting it on my burn. At that point, I just wanted to throw the entire hospital in the trash! Why didn't they know that? Clearly, the wound care person assumed they did. Help them, Father!

I now realized I was in so much pain that I almost went into convulsions. I began to shake and sweat similar to the day I was admitted, except I did not have a fever: I was in excruciating pain. Once the nurses removed the honey patch, which took some of my chest tissue with it, they placed warm gauze and eventually some Silvadene. The pain subsided once the honey patch was removed and the area was moist.

I called Dr. Ro in tears, begging for a referral to a wound care specialist.

"Dr. Ro," I said in tears, "my burn got infected and I have been in the hospital since Thursday with cellulitis in my chest wall."

"Oh no! Did they put you on antibiotics? What hospital?"

"I am being discharged and they just put this honey stuff on my burn, but they did it wrong! Please refer me to a wound care specialist, please! I almost died because this burn will not heal! Please help me!" I cried.

"Oh, Neosho, I am so sorry! I had no idea all of this was going on!" she said.

In my desperation, I begged, while crying, "Can you please refer me to a wound care specialist? Please?"

I have to pause here. In addition to the trauma I am experiencing, I am also forced to beg for help from the person who took an oath to not harm me. Although it was not intentional, I still felt she could have done more.

While I am talking to Dr. Ro, Gwen stepped into the hallway to speak with Dr. Roberts.

She immediately came back in and said, "Hey, Neosho, Dr. Roberts wants you to come see him tomorrow or Wednesday. You don't need to make an appointment, just come. I will come down as well."

I began seeing Dr. Roberts weekly to debride my burn. It seems the slosh that had developed on the unhealed part of the burn was preventing it from healing. The slosh is this mucus-looking spot about as big as a dollar coin. It looked like someone took a deep snort and... Well, you know. Sorry, but not sorry! The visual needed to be vivid so you can understand the severity of the situation.

The debridement was painful, but I was on pain meds and he used this amazing numbing ointment called, lidocaine. I began using it in my everyday wound care, which was a game changer. Dr. Roberts also suggested I put plastic wrap on top of the lidocaine before putting the bandage on. It helped heat the area, thus numbing the area faster. *Thank God for lidocaine!*

The clouds began to part in August. I began meeting with a plastic surgeon, Dr. Davis, regularly. Around the time we were mapping out a plan for reconstruction, Dr. Ro had finally referred me to a wound care specialist, Dr. Finley. My pain meds were immediately increased when I began seeing the wound care specialist. She put me on a twenty-five milligram slow release fentanyl patch in addition to the oxycodone I had been taking for breakthrough pain and the lidocaine for surface pain. Dr. Finley, like others, was shocked at how severe my burn was, but it was not unheard of. Although I could feel Vin healing due to the extreme itching, Dr. Finley prescribed hyperbaric oxygen treatment (HBO) to expedite the healing process. It seemed to be my only option and last hope at reconstruction. One of the biggest obstacles I didn't see coming was the god-awful itching that came with Vin healing from the inside out. Since my reconstruction plan blew up in my face, the itching was quite apropos. When (wo) man plans, well, *you know the rest.*

First, there was a hold up with my insurance approving the HBO treatment. Then, Dr. Davis said since it took the burn so long to fully heal, she believed the vessels in my chest were fried by the radiation, so my first choice of reconstruction was off the table. I felt so defeated! I shared my sadness and frustration with one of my Pink Sisters, Cassie, who I had met in March through a local organization for breast cancer survivors. She highly recommended her plastic surgeon and since I had nothing to lose, I made an appointment. Unfortunately, her plastic surgeon did not do the type of reconstruction I needed, but referred me to a microsurgeon, Dr. Bennett. I was fighting sadness and depression due to so much disappointment and hoped I could find a ray of hope somewhere!

I saw small slivers of light in all this darkness when I started working a temp job at the end of September. The joy of working was short lived because due to the schedule, I was forced to miss Candace and Tye's wedding. To see the photos on Facebook and then to see everyone else's lives moving forward just added to my depression. I was already tired of the pain, the itching, the loneliness, and losing friends. I was just *tired*! I began to imagine a world without me in it. I was not supposed to still be dealing with cancer related issues!

And then the Lord said, "delete people from your Facebook." I thought He said, "delete your Facebook."

"I can't delete my Facebook, God! That is how I get financial help and meals," I pleaded.

"I didn't say delete Facebook. I said delete people! If people's lives are causing you to be suicidal, then you need to remove those images," He explained.

I was obedient and deleted half of my Facebook friends. Of course, the joke was on me yet again 'cause I did not make an announcement or even mention my mental health issues. I just deleted people, which was impulsive and could have been handled better. I now know one of my ADHD traits is impulsivity. That was probably the worst mistake I made throughout my cancer journey. However, I did not know people took social media friendships so seriously, especially when we were friends in real life. I am never going to understand that, but I digressed. Once I stopped seeing so many of life's milestones such as marriage, children, vacations, promotions, awards, and home ownership, I prayed and continued to share my progress on Caring Bridge and in my secret Facebook group. God pulled back the veil of darkness so I could see that weeping or in this case, depression, may endure for a night, but joy comes in the morning,

By November, I was elated to begin HBO and had saved enough money by working the temp job to move. Yup, move number three coming, right up! I appreciated Ms. Jackie for opening up her home to me, but I began to feel as if I had overstayed my welcome. Six months had turned into a year. As excited as I remember being, I now know this move was rushed. I should have been patient and taken my time to find a roommate that was a better fit for my values. Once again, I was begging for people to help me move. I was sure people were tired of my moves at this point, but just like the previous two times, my village showed up. In addition to working and moving, I had an amazing surgeon who believed she could reconstruct my breasts using my stomach!

Dr. Bennett was the perfect surgeon for my reconstruction. She was thorough, innovative, and fearless! She also monitored my HBO treatment closely and despite a few setbacks, any amount of HBO treatment contributed to the success of the surgery. I had no idea how vital HBO was to my reconstruction.

As 2017 came to a close, I was in a good space, but that was relative. I was working, my reconstructive surgery was scheduled for January, and finally, I lived in a place where I could cook. I was still dealing with Vin, but its days were numbered, because January was around the corner. Vin was making work increasingly difficult due to the itch from the pit of hell! In addition to the excruciating itch, if I ran out of pain meds, I would have to cry from the pain. I had to tell my coworkers about the burn, so they would not be alarmed by my tears or on days when my pain meds were kickin' in, I may nod off. I had to assure everyone I worked with that I can work, but that damn burn itched like the dickens!

The itching had gotten so bad at work that I had to leave my desk, go to the bathroom on a different floor, lock myself in the handicapped stall, and beat the hell out of my chest. I would hit Vin while jumping up and down, running in place, crying, and singing gospel music. I hit my chest until it hurt! The relief I felt when the pain kicked in was indescribable. I would often thank God for the itching and the pain because both were proof that I am healing and that the end is near. Just when I thought 2017 was the worst year of my life, 2018 said, "*Oh yeah! Hold my beer. Watch me work!*"

CHAPTER 13

ROLLIN' IN THE DIEP

———

2018 was my year of renewal! I started the year looking forward to my new boobs using the DIEP flap reconstruction (flat tummy), getting back on my feet professionally, and dating. Yet, again, the joke was on me! Let's run it down, shall we.

By the end of 2018, I'd undergone an eleven-hour surgery and a four-hour surgery totaling fifteen hours of surgery in one night, then three months later another five-hour surgery, and later in the year, three revisions with a whopping total of five—yes, *five*—surgeries. I lost not one, not two, but three friends in three months, oh, and a brother.

How did I go from being excited about getting rid of Vin, that god-awful burn, and getting new boobs to all of these challenges? Well, I wrote a story about it. Wanna read it? Here it goes...

As I reflected on 2017, I wrote this in my online Caring Bridge journal:

"My entire year has been about this BURN! This burn has been the bane of my existence...literally! I mean, it's so horrible, I have to laugh to keep from losing my mind. I have had a life-threatening infection, debilitating breakdowns, and to

top it all off, I've lost some of my most supportive friends."
(Ponder, 2017)

In January 2018, I was comfortable in my new place and working the temp job. I was scheduled to have the DIEP flap breast reconstruction surgery around January 18. DIEP flap reconstruction is a microsurgery that involves removing the skin and fat from the stomach and reconnecting the blood vessels in the flap to the chest (breastcancer.org, 2021). Similar to a cesarean, it required an epidural to control the pain due to a hip-to-hip incision. Due to my burn, part of my surgery was spent excising the burn, which would allow for the flap of skin and fat to be placed over my left chest and my armpit, thus getting rid of the burn.

Honestly, my surgeon wasn't 100 percent sure the flap would take due to the severity of the burn, but I explained that the way my faith was set up, I had no worry or fear. This was a big surgery! So, to recap, part of my stomach skin and fat was placed on the right side, which did not have cancer and keep in mind that I chose to remove the right breast as a precaution. The focus was really on getting rid of the burn.

Side bar: Do you know what could happen if you ignore one of your children? Well, just keep that in mind when reading what happened next.

I prayed the DIEP flap surgery would free me of the burn. Well, just remember that God is not only the original king of comedy, but he is also the emperor of irony, *and* the president of petty. Unfortunately, my surgeon injured her knee skiing and had to postpone my surgery until February 7. I was devastated at first, but then realized the silver lining was that I could keep working! I thought, "okay, 2018! See, I thought you were letting me down already." I used the time to prepare for surgery. I knew I would need help and my current roommate is not the type to check on me. I immediately enlisted the help of my best friend, John. I was so thankful that John lived in the DC area, especially since he was the closest person to family I had nearby.

My friendship with John could be a book in and of itself, which I hope to write one day. We had been through so much since high school and I now realize that all we had gone through had brought us to this point. When I was diagnosed, John was a calming presence. He lived almost an hour away, but still made the trip down to go to a few doctor appointments with me. I was not surprised when he shaved his head in solidarity with me, because that is who John is. He is a steady, reliable presence.

The surgery I was about to undergo did not have a high mortality rate, but I would be under anesthesia for more than ten hours and would have a six to eight-week recovery time, so that made me rethink some things. While I did not expect any dramatic complications, and unlike many of my pink sisters, I did not create a living will. Honestly, I just thought it was too morbid. I had a best friend of more than twenty years who served our country as an officer in the Army and knows me better than most of my family. I knew he would make sure everything was in proper order if that moment came. However, I did not consider the fact there was a possibility that on-the-spot medical decisions might need to be made.

I did not feel comfortable with my family making those decisions from 1,100 miles away in Kansas City, so I asked John to serve as my medical proxy. I knew it was a big ask and that he would need to speak with Seth, his husband. I was so appreciative of Seth supporting John's decision to serve as my medical proxy, which included coming to the hospital with me the day of my surgery. He immediately began asking questions, such as what time he needed be at the hospital, what time does the surgery begin and end, and how long I would be in the hospital. What I was not prepared for was what he asked next.

"Hey, Neosh, what time do you want me to come to your house the night before your surgery?" he asked.

"Huh? What do you mean?" I asked.

"Well, you need me to take you to the hospital, right?"

"Oh, yeah, I would really appreciate it!" I exclaimed. I had not thought about it, to be honest. I was so busy making sure I had things for my recovery that I didn't stop and think about who was taking me!

"Okay, well you have to be there at like 6 a.m., right? So, I will have to stay the night. I am not waking up that early to drive down to DC," he said with a laugh.

"So, you are coming here to take me to the hospital and then go to work?"

"Nah, girl, Imma work from there," he laughed again.

"Oh wow... Thank you so much! Please thank Seth for me as well."

John's willingness to spend an entire day at the hospital with me was either a testament of our friendship or a testament that he wanted to play hooky from work. Either way, I'll take it! We show up for each other even in times of disconnect and strife. I mean he sent me birthday emails while in combat!

In addition to having a best friend who had accepted the task of deciding my fate if I was incapacitated, I was blessed to have so many prayer warriors on this journey with me. When I went for my mastectomy, I received a voicemail from my pastor's intern, Nick. When I was in the hospital, suffering from the burn, Nick drove to DC from Maryland to pray with me. So, when it was time for my big DIEP flap surgery, I knew exactly who I wanted to pray with me before that long surgery. If you have a major life event, it is imperative that you have a prayer warrior. Granted, I know some amazingly, anointed people who have prayed with me for various accomplishments and hardships, but I believe God placed Nick in my life to pray over my surgeries. I went into my surgery covered by the blood of Jesus!

Speaking of blood, after eleven hours of surgery, I awoke groggy and in pain. The first person I see is John.

"Hey, babe. You did great! I've been updating the fam," he said. He was trying to be reassuring.

"Ouch," I struggled to say. It was hard to breathe, let alone to get a word out.

"Huh? What did you say?" he asked.

"Ouch. John... It hurts."

"Yeah, but you did good. Everyone is proud of you."

"Get someone. It hurts. I'm supposed to be achy, but it hurts. Something is wrong," I said.

As I was saying this, the nurse noticed me struggling to speak and rushed over.

"Ms. Ponder," she said, "How are you feeling?"

"Ouch. It hurts," I moaned.

"Well, you have had a big surgery," she said as she used a doppler to check for blood flow in my breasts. After she checked my blood flow and hearing me in pain, she explained the use of the pain button. John pushed it, but the nurse said

I had to do it myself and said she would check on me in a few. After the nurse left, I dozed off.

John had my parents on the phone as I was waking up, about an hour later.

"It hurts," I said.

"Hi, baby!" Pam screamed.

"Hi baby. Glad you are okay. Get some rest. God bless," Rodger said.

I looked at John and told him something was wrong. I remembered being told I would feel like I just got hit by a bus: sore, achy, but not like I felt.

"No, John, get her. Something is wrong," I said while gasping for air. I felt really sharp sticks or cuts. It was painful and nothing like what I was told it would be like. I knew something was wrong.

When the nurse came back, I said, "It hurts."

Using the doppler to check for blood flow, she noticed there was little flow to the right side and some swelling in my right breast. Then, another nurse checked and noticed the slight swelling and sent the first nurse to get the doctor, a surgical resident named Corey. I only remember his name because he had great hair and I joked about him looking like a McDreamy. It's funny how you remember little details like that while you're hopped up on pain meds.

When Dr. Corey checked using the doppler, he too noticed the lack of blood flow on the right side. When he checked my incisions, they all noticed my right breast had swelled even more just in the short time between the nurses checking and him checking. He then noticed my stitches were ripping due to the swelling! So, in a rapid response, he ordered the nurse to get a suture kit and with the scissors in that kit, he cut the stitches across the bottom of my right breast. As he cut, I began to exhale in relief. If you are thinking what I hope you are, then you are absolutely correct! The pain I kept telling them I felt was real. The stitches were ripping my skin!

In a race against time, Dr. Corey covered me up and told the nurses to get my surgeon, Dr. Bennett, back to the hospital and then turned to me and said, "Okay, Ms. Ponder, we are going to take you back into the OR to see what is going on with your flap."

"She has to have another surgery?" John asked. "I want to update her family." He had been standing by during all the commotion. I was in and out of consciousness by this point, so I am not sure what was said after I heard John ask that question.

I was quickly wheeled back into the operating room and when I woke up, there was a recovery nurse standing over me. I was completely zonked, but I do remember his name was Shane and I asked him if he was named after the movie. He laughed and said no, but he was familiar with the reference. He explained John had to go, but the surgery went well and I was in recovery. As Shane walked away, I whined, "Don't go, Shane!" He laughed. You have to see the movie to get it. I was out of it!

Then, a resident checked on me. She delivered some devastating news, which I was not ready for due to me still struggling to come out of the anesthesia.

"Ms. Ponder, how are you feeling?" she asked.

"I'm okay," I said in a dry, groggy voice.

"Can you rate your pain for me?"

"Um, like an eight," I moaned.

"Okay, we will see what we can do about your pain," she said.

Then she casually continued, "So, when we took you back into the OR, Dr. Bennett tried for four hours to save your flap, but was unsuccessful," she said, in the most stoic voice ever. Her voice had no compassion or empathy. It sounded like; *it is what it is.* "Dr. Bennett has you on the blood thinner, heparin, and we are gonna put you in the ICU for close monitoring. She was on her feet for eleven hours and then another four hours, so she is home, but will come by tomorrow to discuss possible next steps," she continued.

"What do you mean?" I asked.

"Well, since your flap failed—"

"Failed? Huh? What does that mean?" I asked.

"Since the blood stopped flowing in your right flap, the breast you had problems with, she tried to repair it for four hours, but the blood flow was not restored, so..." she explained.

"So..." I began to feel the tears, "so, I only have one?"

"Yeah. Your flap failed, so the doctor will discuss other options with you. Okay, now let me take a look," she said as if she had not just delivered the news that survivors fear most about this type of surgery.

As she was checking me, I began to cry. My chest was tightly wrapped, so I could not tell what my breasts look like. As she was checking me, I do not remember one word of comfort. I mean, I didn't expect her to cry with me, but dang, can you at least fake some compassion?

I had entered the hospital the morning of Wednesday, February 7. My surgery began at 7 a.m. It was 11 hours long, which means I was in recovery around 8 p.m. I woke up in pain around 11 p.m. and was back in surgery for 4 more hours. I was back in recovery around 6 a.m. When I woke up in recovery and met Nurse Shane, it was roughly 4 p.m.

When I heard the news of my failed flap, it was around 6 p.m. When I got to ICU, it was around eight p.m. I only know those times because someone told me.

I do not remember February 8, 2018.

CHAPTER 14

IT WAS THE WORST OF TIMES AND THEN IT GOT *WORSER*

———

My DIEP flap surgery was part of the 1 percent to 2 percent of flaps that failed (Heidekrueger et al., 2021). I checked into the hospital without breasts only to wake up after a whopping fifteen total hours of surgery, two surgeries in one day, with *one* boob? God's got jokes for real!

I spent seven days in the ICU on a heparin drip to insure no more blood clots would form. My surgeon, Dr. Bennett, was very thorough and on top of my treatment. In the days following my marathon surgery, she sent several specialists, including a rheumatologist and hematologist, to examine me and run tests. She also checked in with my nurses throughout the night so I didn't sleep much.

One nurse said, "Oh your doctor makes sure we are on top of your care. She is very thorough!" Hearing that gave me a sense of peace and comfort.

After a few days of grieving my failed flap, I was able to laugh and enjoy the Winter Olympics. The nurses would take breaks in my room for medal count updates and to watch the events with me. We bonded over our love of Shaun White and the National Anthem. I was probably one of just a few patients in my ICU area who was awake most of the time, so they knew when we'd won the gold because I would belt out the Star-Spangled Banner. I mean enjoying this great American pastime took my mind off of the epidural, heparin drip, catheter, and of course, Solo Dolo. Yes, I named my single, Solo Dolo. On my fifth or sixth day, I began to get a bit antsy. A week is a long time. I was ready to go home!

I was looking forward to getting out of the hospital so I could see Michael. The week before my surgery, January 31, he called and told me he was diagnosed with lymphoma. I was aware of his other health challenges, but this was jarring. I knew he had passed out while in Germany a few months prior, but I thought he was fine. I was nervous, but I remembered all I'd been through on my journey. I reminded him of that during our call.

"We've been here before, right?" I said.

"Yes, we have," he replied.

"So, you just have to make the decision to fight. You have come too far to let cancer beat you. Plus, chile, we got a trip to take!" I said, reminding him of his offer to take me to Switzerland on one of his flights. He primarily flew internationally and had brought me Swiss chocolate back once.

One day, when I stayed with him, I was having a pity party about all the things I had yet to do, like have a baby, get married, and visit Africa. When I told him I still hadn't used my passport, he said, "Well, chile, that's an easy fix!"

I guess that was a perk of having a friend who is a international flight attendant. He was really on my mind the entire time I was in the hospital. I had to convince him not to visit due to germs.

I was released from the hospital on Wednesday, February 14. Not only was it Valentine's Day and my grandfather's 101st birthday, but it was also Ash Wednesday. My friend from church, Yolanda, picked me up around 6 p.m. She had volunteered to spend my first few days out of the hospital with me, for which I was so grateful. I could hardly walk and had three drains and a pain pump pinned to the inside of my shirt. Once they got me in the car, she asked where the pharmacy was to get my meds.

"Oh, they filled them in the hospital. I want to go to church," I replied.

"Church? Girl, you just got out of the hospital!"

"And that is exactly why I want to get my ashes!" I said with a chuckle. It hurt to laugh, but felt good at the same time.

"Uh... Ok, girl," she said in disbelief.

When I arrived, I was thankful that so many who were familiar with my diagnosis were on hand to assist me. I attend a mega church so the sanctuary is huge. I walked as close to the altar as I could get. Yolanda ran to get the minister to women. She prayed and put the ashes on my forehead. I knew this was necessary for me to properly heal.

My village was amazing, but I knew it was God. Every time someone showed up for me, I was reminded of Deuteronomy 31:8 "He would never leave nor forsake you." I felt God's hand in so many acts of kindness and selflessness from family and friends.

My auntie, Renee, called Michael my angel because he took me in when no one else would. I mean, we had been friends for almost ten years, so he had been there for me so many times. The summer of 2012, he fed me from his job at a bar and filled up my gas tank for just giving him a ride home from work. We were family. So, when I didn't hear from him much while I was in the hospital, I figured he was exhausted from his own chemo treatment. I told him he didn't need to come to the hospital due to his compromised immune system from the chemo, but he sent a text on February 10, checking on me and to see when he could come visit. I told him I would call him when I got home, which I did, but he didn't answer.

On Saturday, February 17, he sent a text, "Hey love. How are you?"

"I'm okay," I replied. I had zero energy to text more than that.

"Okay good," he replied. I had no idea how significant that text would be to me.

When I called a few days later, he sounded super sleepy, so I figured he would call me when he got up or the next day. Something didn't feel right. I mean I am recovering from surgery, trying to stay on top of meds, and praying my incisions don't open and yet, I had not heard from Michael, which is not like him. We were always in constant communication. After a few days, when I didn't hear from him about visiting me, I sent him a text, "Hey. Come see me. I miss you!"

Then, the worst of times got worse.

I received a response that said, "Hey. This is Michael's sister, Rose. He isn't able to do so."

In a series of texts, I said, "I had a feeling! Can you just tell me if he is okay, please."

At this point, I was in tears, but I couldn't cry like I wanted to because of my stomach incision. I felt powerless waiting on her response.

As my texts continued, I began to go down a rabbit hole of emotions. I began to think that my friend was dead and she didn't want to tell me.

"Is there any way I can find out how he's doing?" I asked.

"Please call me when you can," I pleaded in a follow up text.

After calling and being sent to voicemail, I sent another text, "I am Neosho. I lived with him when I was going through chemo. I've been in the hospital for my breast reconstruction. I just got out last week. I told him not to visit me in the hospital because I thought he was going through chemo."

Finally, she responded with more info: "He is okay. Has a long uphill battle, but we are a family of faith and trust in God. We are dealing with a lot today. I prefer to speak at a later time. You can call tomorrow if you like."

Then, the worst of times got *worser.*

I continued to check in with Michael's sister over the next couple of weeks. Since I was still healing from my surgery, I decided to spend my thirty-eighth birthday, March 9, the National Holiday, at the Blacksonian. The next day, while getting a birthday mani pedi, I received a call from Renard, me and Michael's mutual friend.

"Hey love. What are you doin' today?"

"Hey! I'm at the nail shop, so don't tell me no bad news: it's my birthday," I said.

"Yeah, I just wanted to call and wish you a happy birthday, love. Just give me a call tomorrow. What are y'all doin tonight? "

A Wrinkle in Time was released on my birthday, so I invited some girlfriends to dinner and a movie the next day. I knew when I saw Renard's name on my phone, but I tried to block it out and enjoy my friends.

The next day in church, my phone started blowing up. I received Facebook messages and posts on my wall from people I didn't know. The confirmation came from my friend, Simon, in a text message.

"Oh my gosh, Neosho, not Michael! Are you okay?"

I went to the altar to pray for Michael's family. I struggled to kneel, but I got down there. While praying, God literally showed me our highlight reel. The more I saw, the less I cried. When I left church, I immediately called Renard. After some cryptic dialogue, he said, "Michael is no longer with us." I thanked him for telling me, but I needed to call someone else and get more details.

Then I called a friend who lived with Michael at one point and checked in on me when I stayed at Michael's. He told me a lot more about what happened. He explained some details of Michael's passing, but the most expected news was that my friend passed away on my thirty-eighth birthday, March 9, 2018! I was shocked and just devastated. Michael seemed to be getting better and then took a turn. His sister never gave me much information about his location or specific condition, but I learned later from friends that the lymphoma metastasized to his brain. There are no words.

A week later, just one month out of the ICU, I traveled to Chicago to say goodbye to my friend. I did not care whether I could travel or not; I knew I needed to be there. I was wheeled through the airport and our amazing friends made sure I did not have to walk too much while in Chicago. At times, I cannot believe how resilient my body was during this time, then I remember Isaiah 53:5, "By His stripes, you are healed." God makes no mistakes, but this was only the beginning.

After healing from the DIEP flap surgery and preparing for my next reconstruction at the end of May, I learned *onest again* I had to move. My living situation was not conducive for healing.

On May 8, received a text from one of my sorors and sista-friends, Natasha.

"Neosho, our girl Tiffany Johnson passed this morning."

"Oh my god!" I replied. I immediately called Natasha, "No, please no! What! Oh my god!" I completely broke down.

"Are you okay?" she asked, choking back tears herself.

"Was she at home or in the hospital?" I asked.

"She was at a breakfast meeting and collapsed," she said.

Natasha stayed on the phone with me to give me words of comfort while crying too. We cried together for about ten minutes and then I realized I needed to gather myself, because I was about to leave for my pre-op appointment for my next surgery.

I was devastated! Tiffany was like a big sister to me. I used to tell her I wanted to be like her when I grow up. We always laughed about it. She picked me up from chemo, gave me consulting jobs to help with my bills, and whenever an opportunity came up that would be good for me, she always shared it with me. I participated in that BET campaign because of her! Tiffany Johnson was always supportive and inspiring!

Times were still getting worse and it wasn't even six months into 2018. I could not attend Tiffany's funeral because I was delivering the commencement address at my high school in Kansas City. I was honored to be the speaker since I was the class speaker at my own graduation twenty years earlier. This was a bittersweet experience. The bright side was that I found a place to live before I left. My plan was to move

June 1, but as you have read thus far, most of my plans are derailed. The young lady I expected to rent from rescinded the rental! She claimed she expected my deposit before I left for Kansas City on May 10, but she never told me that. It was a mess, so when I returned from KC, I prepared for my next reconstructive surgery. Solo Dolo will be no more! C'mon silver lining!!

For the reconstruction of my right boob, Dr. Bennett decided to use the latissimus dorsi muscle (lat flap) in my back. Isn't the human body amazing? The latissimus is the muscle on your back right around from your breast at the bra line. I have never been more thankful for being a thick girl! If I were thin or fit, this surgery would not be possible. Unfortunately, for many skinny and fit women, DIEP flaps and lat flaps are not an option because they don't have enough fat and tissue to transfer.

Like my previous surgery, I received an epidural, but instead of it being in my lower back, it was in my upper back, which was interesting. The surgery was about five hours without any complications, hallelujah! I woke up with two healthy boobs and they stayed that way. *Won't He do it!* I spent five days in a regular hospital room, which was a different experience than ICU. The nurses in the regular rooms were far busier and less attentive, but they were really nice.

The day I was released, I noticed my back was itching where the epidural tape had been. It was still a bit numb, but I felt an itch. When I reached to scratch, I noticed something was wet on my hand. I asked the nurse to look and she said there were blisters down my back where the tegaderm tape was for those five days. I knew I was allergic to the clear, hospital adhesive tape, but had never had an issue with tegaderm.

I just shook my head and said, yup, the universe isn't ready for me to be great.

While recovering from the lat flap surgery, I had to keep looking for a place to live. I was literally visiting potential places with drains hanging out of me. It was exhausting! I finally found a place with two other professional Black women and with my own garage. The young lady I was currently living with either turned off the HVAC system before traveling out of town or it stopped working right before my move-in date. Unfortunately, the central air system was in her room in the basement. I did not feel comfortable entering her space. So, there we were, me and several of my ministry friends, on a Sunday in July in the dead heat of summer with no fan or air conditioning. I felt like God was tryin' to tell me somethin'!

I moved into a townhouse and since I had my own private area on the ground floor near the garage, I only shared common areas and rarely saw the other women. It was extremely small but very cozy. I also had a small storage room, which saved me money on storage. This place was my first sigh of relief with moving. John was the relocation conductor as always, my brothers from church did a lot of heavy lifting, and my girlfriends were on hand for everything else. It was a well-oiled machine at this point, since this was move number four in two years!

The week before my move, at the end of June, I learned of the passing of yet another friend who I met on a church retreat years earlier. He would check on me and pray with me during breakfast before church. He was also one of the friends I could call to go to a party or event with me. I was distraught! This was my third friend to pass away in three months. I was struggling to understand. He was young, healthy, active, and a positive presence. I began to feel that God was taking people who had helped me along my cancer journey.

It seemed like, just when things were looking up, then boom: another tragedy. I tried to get back to some sense of normalcy after yet another move and grieving the loss of yet another friend. On the upside, shortly after I moved, I found a temp job doing data entry. This allowed me to continue to heal without the worries of employment for the time being.

Since I had two healthy breasts and was healed from the major surgeries, my surgeon decided that my revisions should start in August. My first revision surgery was set for August 18. This involved fat grafting and fixing any small things from the previous two surgeries. There are typically two or three revisions done as outpatient surgeries, meaning no overnight stays. Just as I was looking forward to my revision surgery, here comes the next curveball. Well, you already know; if something *can* go wrong, it will.

This was one of those times when I understood God's timing. Yes, he is the president of petty and the original king of comedy, but the irony of his timing was impeccable. I learned a valuable lesson in August 2018, to not get too comfortable and to always be open to receiving blessings from others, especially family. And just when I thought 2018 was the worst year, it got even *worser!*

But that's what I get for thinking!

As I was getting excited about phase two of my reconstruction on August 18, my fellow cancer patient and brother, Victor, knew I had been struggling financially, so he sent me money the first week of August 2018. Although he'd offered a few times throughout my journey, it was the first time since college that I had accepted his offer to give me money. I figured he was getting sentimental since the anniversary of Gene's passing was days away. Something nudged me to accept the money. God speaks in mysterious ways.

By this time, Victor had been living with multiple myeloma for nearly eleven years. His health had been declining over the past year, but still, after every surgery, he was calling me to check my meds and progress. Due to his condition, he was a bit of an authority on pain meds. He was like my cancer partner. No one in our family truly understood the toll that disease takes on your mental and physical health.

On August 7, I received a call from my Uncle Gary who I had just spoken to for his birthday the day before.

"Hey Uncle Gary!"

"Hey Neosho. How are you? Did I catch you at a bad time?" he asked.

"No, I'm just sitting here watching TV. What's up?" I responded in a jovial tone.

"Well... Victor passed away this evening," he said.

Well, damn! Times had definitely gotten *worser!*

It took some processing for sure. I knew he didn't have long when he stopped receiving visitors and when he would video chat with me, his camera would be off. My oldest brother, Vincent, had moved from LA to KC to take care of Victor after our father passed in 2016. Vincent told me Victor wasn't looking too good and was barely walking to the bathroom. My brothers' mother sent me money for my plane ticket, which I really appreciated.

My phase two surgery was postponed due to Victor's passing. Clearly it was God's plan because the rescheduled date was the two-year anniversary of my first chemo infusion, August 23. And remember, it was also my maternal grandmother's birthday. God is really the emperor of irony! This was such a blessing, since I had just lost my brother. I refused to see the negative in any situation. Not the way *my* faith is set up, chile!

My surgery was supposed to be outpatient, but I asked if I could stay the night for observation. When I got to the room, I was told everything went well and then, it hit me. I began to cry. The nurse asked what was wrong.

"I wanna talk to my brother!" I said in tears. This was the first surgery I'd woken up from and couldn't call Victor.

"Where is your phone? It's okay, I will call him for you," she said with so much compassion.

"You can't. He died two weeks ago!" I said in a full ugly cry.

The nurse was so sweet and accommodating. I cried uncontrollably for about twenty minutes until I finally called someone. But it wasn't the same. I just wanted to throw the whole year away!

When I thought about a loss of that magnitude, I began to pray. My prayer took me back to one of my online journal entries on the Caring Bridge site. This is what I wrote the morning before the surgery:

"Every time I go into the hospital, I am reminded of why I have not found a full-time job. God is preparing me for the ULTIMATE opportunity, but it won't be revealed until I complete my breast reconstruction. This war has been full of battles. My most recent battle has been the loss of my "Partner in Cancer", my brother. He won his war and was called home to

be with our dad and God, 2 weeks ago. It was not as difficult as I thought. He fought his own war for 11 years! I am at peace with it. I know God is moving me through these valleys for a reason...so here is a regular convo I have with God:

Me: I GET IT, you are preparing me for greater...but these bills, Lord.

God: I GOT YOU. I AM SENDING ANGELS TO HELP YOU GET THROUGH THIS WAR, CAUSE THE BATTLE IS NOT YOURS!

Me: Thank you!

See, I am not worried. I am not afraid. I will worship and thank God for angels like YOU!" (Ponder, 2018)

When 2018 began, I felt a sense of hope; there was a light at the end of the tunnel. I truly believed it would be a year of transformation and renewal. It was, but not in the way I expected, which had become a theme throughout this journey. My body was transformed but that was expected. Due to the year-long radiation burn, my faith wavered. The renewal came when I overcame a surgical complication and survived. While this was not the transformation and renewal I expected when I rang in the new year of 2018, what I gained through transformation and renewal was priceless.

Despite the devastating losses, I can truly say that God sends us angels when we need them most. God has said, "Well done, my good and faithful servant" to the very people who gave me shelter, paid my bills, and prayed for me throughout this journey. When you have gone through all that I went through in 2018, you understand why we praise him in the good times and bad. There were moments in 2018 that I thought I was being punished for something because losses of this magnitude must have been a punishment. That is when I realized that although I suffered losses, they were not about me. When your work on this Earth is done, then it is finished.

CHAPTER 15

IT'S LONELY AT THE TOP

By the end of 2018, I had survived five surgeries, the loss of three friends and a brother, and yet another move shortly after my third surgery. I must have been hitting my stride at this thing called the "new normal" because before my diagnosis any one of these would have destroyed me. The losses and trauma I endured in 2018 tested my faith, rocked my confidence, and bruised my spirit, but I persevered. I trusted God, listened to the doctors, and leveraged every connection I had in hopes of getting a job. The more licks I took, the more were thrown at me. I just kept bobbing and weaving, which revealed a feeling I had not dealt with previously on my journey: loneliness.

It didn't hit me just how single I was until I was done with treatment and major surgeries. Single and lonely are not where you want to be at thirty-eight, let me tell ya! I figured I would casually date to get myself back out there on the dating scene, but I realized that I was not the same person I was before my diagnosis in April 2016. In addition to being two years older, I had become more self-aware, which tapped into my vulnerability, an area I did not want to acknowledge. I often told people cancer did not make me stronger, it made me more vulnerable. As I was coming to grips with the revelation of vulnerability, I also realized that sometimes, in a crowded room, you can still feel alone. That is how I would describe my life after treatment and surgery.

Dating was a damn chore, sheesh! I had never been *ghosted* and borderline stalked like that before, my goodness. I never put my name on the apps, but one guy called and heard my name on my voicemail greeting and Googled me! Chile, his crazy ass sent me a text.

"Why didn't you tell me you had cancer?"

"Excuse me? Sir, I just met you *online!* And how do you know my business?" I exclaimed.

He said, "Because I Googled you." *Full stop.*

Now, I may be a little rusty at this dating thing, but calling someone out because they didn't disclose a *past* cancer diagnosis is a flag on the play!

"Why would you do that?" I asked.

"Did you have cancer or not?" he asked as if he had a right to know.

"If I did, it was my story to share. That is not cool and a complete turn-off," I said.

Honestly, I am not sure what he said next, because I immediately *blocked* him. I felt violated. I couldn't trust someone who would Google me instead of getting to know me first. We talked a couple of times, but never met in person. There was no reason to do that. Now, while you are thinking I overreacted, but what he did next was textbook stalker!

A couple of days after I blocked him, this fool had the nerve to text me from a different number as if nothing had happened! I asked if he knew who it was and he said, "yes I do, it's Dr. Ponder." Y'all, I almost lost it! *Blocked.* I had to block like three different numbers for this guy.

About a year later, I told my roommate that story, thinking we were just sharing our crazy dating app stories. Y'all... She pulled out her phone, showed me his picture, and asked, "Is this him?"

"Oh, hell naw!" I yelled.

She had actually gone on a date with him and saw so many red flags. This was new territory for me. *Lawwwd*, we both could have been on the ID Channel! I did not give up, but I was definitely skeptical going forward.

I met another guy on an app who invited me to play Top-Golf. It was a real date! We played for hours. It was so much fun. He even kissed me goodnight and it was a great kiss. Then, I never heard from him again! I was like, *where they do that at?* It was nice to be kissed, but the kiss reminded me that I had not had sex in over two years.

My first sexual experience was with a guy I met at an event. We hung out for a couple of months. He worked in law enforcement, so his schedule was unorthodox. The night I disclosed my breast cancer history, it was almost like a movie! He kissed all of my scars, carried me to his bedroom, and took his time with me. I had forgotten what it felt like to be desired. I had not been touched sexually by a man since June 23, 2016. Hey, when it had been that long, you never forget! After that encounter, I lost interest in him. His schedule was difficult to plan around and he reached out less and less until finally: radio silence. It seemed like we both only wanted one thing and I was fine with that. Even when we were together, I felt lonely. That sexual experience was just another step in my quest for normalcy.

Another milestone I achieved by the end of 2018 was consistent employment. I have to admit that not working all day while the rest of the world is working is the loneliest place to be in. I had not worked in an office environment since 2011 when I began my doctoral program. I began to regret my decision to not work and teach on campus during my doctoral studies. When you are struggling to stay afloat, while dealing with so many non-health related factors, you get that *'wish'* factor, but not like the Cedric the Entertainer joke on *The Original Kings of Comedy,* but the *'wish you had taken that job'* or *'wish you had returned that call,'* then you start singing your *"shouldas, couldas, wouldas."* I spent a lot of time thinking about my missed opportunities. I prayed I would take advantage of the next opportunity and I did!

I was afforded an amazing opportunity to work part-time in an academic environment while interacting with students and using my communications expertise. While it wasn't the ideal role, I enjoyed helping the students and the program staff with professional development events and social media visibility. It was the perfect position for where I was in my journey. For a time, I had forgotten about my previous health disparity until it was time for my next surgical revision in December 2018. I had prayed about it and even though I was not worried about issues with my job, I still felt nervous about my supervisor knowing such personal information about me.

I asked my supervisor if I could speak with her. She said she would come to my office in an hour.

"I just wanted to talk to you about something," I said.

"Oh okay. What's going on?" she responded.

She had come into my office with her lunch, so I immediately knew it would not be the professional setting for such a personal disclosure.

"Well, in 2016, a year after finishing school, I found a lump in my left breast," I began.

She quickly interrupted, "Oh, I know. I Googled you!" she said with a chuckle.

"*Okay*. Well, I just wanted you to know that I am having an outpatient procedure," I continued, but was a bit shocked at her response.

It was extremely uncomfortable for me to share this very personal information. This was when I began to notice the emotional sensitivity I had toward my cancer journey. I had been through so much that year alone, so when she reacted that way, I felt robbed of my opportunity to tell my truth. This was my way of attempting to lean into my vulnerability. I may have had different feelings if I tried to hide it or if we were talking in general about illness and it came up. I asked to speak with her in my office because she shared an office with another colleague, and the woman I shared an office with was gone for the day.

I explained my procedure was outpatient, but I kept further details of my journey private. Although I know so much can be found online, I felt kind of weird by her chuckling about already knowing about my breast cancer. Now, I do not believe my supervisor's response was malicious. I really liked my job and tried to keep things as professional as possible, however we developed a camaraderie that may have opened the door to that level of comfort. Things were starting to look up in several areas of my life. I enjoyed my part-time job, liked where I lived, and was getting more social.

I had been living in my new place for a few months and despite a few bumps here and there, I felt good. I loved the privacy of my personal space and secure garage for my car. When Uncle Gary and Aunt Anita visited DC, they were excited to see my new place. They, too, liked the privacy I had. Later that night, after I dropped them off at their hotel,

I returned home. This was the first place I lived in a while that didn't give me anxiety when I returned. It was a Friday night and I was wiped out. I loved showing family around DC, but due to my many surgeries, I was always exhausted at the end of the day. I laid my head on the pillow and thought, "I finally feel at home."

The next morning, I woke up to a to group text from the landlord, that said, "Hello everyone. After deep prayer and careful consideration, I have decided to rent the entire house out to one person/family. If you are interested in renting the entire house, then please let me know in a separate message. If everyone could find a place by the end of February, I would like to have it rented by spring." It was October. I had just moved in that July. Another one bites the dust.

I don't know about the others in the house, but I was devastated. I specifically chose that place because I could live there for at least a year. I also communicated that when I met with the landlord. She said I could sign a six-month lease to make sure I liked it and then sign another six-month lease in January. Once again, I felt like the rug was being pulled from beneath me. Talk about *TI-RED*.

Since my diagnosis, I'd moved five times. Yes, I was tired of moving, but I was more tired of seeing people's lives move forward and mine move laterally. I felt like I was healed and I was able to make ends meet, but that was about it. I was not progressing the way I expected I would be at this point in time. I was ready to work full-time, but I was starting to think my PhD was hindering me from getting a job. I had friends suggest I remove it from my resume, but I could not lie about my level of education. It's lonely at the top! There was no easy answer. And then, in February 2019, in E-True Cancer Story fashion, I moved again! I found a place that came with my own living area and since I had some anxiety about my previous situation, I signed a one-year lease. In a weird turn of events, I met a guy within two weeks of moving! I was not sure if things were getting better since so much had happened, but I decided to just go with it.

When you have been through as much as I had been through, you become apathetic to things that would excite the average woman. After about three weeks of non-stop communication and planned dates, he pulled away. I figured that was a sign from God. He eventually reached out and apologized, explaining that things were moving too fast for him. This newfound layer of vulnerability allowed me to see things differently. I was hurt and I was okay with saying I was hurt, but I think more than anything, I was lonely. I totally understood with things moving a bit fast, but he set the pace. I think I got accustomed to having something to do and somewhere to go and now I am back to it being just me and Jesus.

I took the shock and pain of being alone and poured it into volunteering at my church and working my part-time job. I was also beginning to understand God's humor in that situation. I didn't think I truly understood it until I started dating. As the old adage goes, God doesn't always give you what you ask for; he gives you what you need. I came to understand the caveat to that as well. He only gives you what you need if you can handle it. He knows if he had given me an amazing job and loving relationship at that time, I wouldn't appreciate them the same as when he blesses me with what I need in due time. This journey has increased my patience as well.

My loneliness was not limited to intimate companionship, but also friendship. I ended a twenty-five-year friendship because I was in it alone. I found that many different relationships were one-sided. I was depleted emotionally and sought comfort in random connections that never produced any substance. I'd meet guys and they would complain about my vocabulary and interests. While that may sound weird, it was even more weird to experience. I literally had a guy say, "You don't have to use big words with me," because I said I wanted to be accommodating. I can't remember what the conversation was exactly, but I remembered his reaction to a word I used regularly. It was hard! I started to doubt myself and modify my vernacular when I'd meet someone new. That did not last long! I refused to misrepresent myself. I am who I am.

As my journey increased my patience, it also enhanced my layers of vulnerability. I was no longer equipped to be hard like I once was. I genuinely cared about how others felt about me. My feelings were important to me, but it also made me feel weak. I had no idea what was going on with me! I prayed to God for direction and understanding. The only response I got was loneliness. As I spent more time communing with God, I began to understand the saying, "It's lonely at the top." I was finally healthy, living in a stable place, and was able to pay my bills, but I was alone. My faith in God continued to sustain me.

CHAPTER 16

THERE'S NO PLACE LIKE HOME

———

"If we know ourselves, we're always home anywhere."
—GLINDA, THE GOOD WITCH OF THE SOUTH, *THE WIZ*

Throughout my cancer journey, I have struggled with finding a place to call home. I am still shocked at how I made it through chemo while being forced to move. The stresses of fighting for your life while homeless can make most people give up and lose faith. I believe it made me fight harder. I fought for the life I expected to create for myself after finishing school. I fought for the family I had yet to create. I fought for the work that could make a lasting impact on our communities. I fought for the physical appearance I once had, only to discover I would never look like that again. Then, in 2019, when the fighting seemed to cease, I felt lost. I found myself fighting for the comforts of home and unbeknownst to me, that fight began within me.

When I began seeing a new primary care physician, Dr. Ahmed, I had so many physical and mental health concerns that I didn't know where to begin. I did not know whether I was coming or going. It was difficult to complete anything and every ache, pain, or lump made me paranoid. This was also a time when I had no upcoming treatments or procedures, so I was unsure of what to do next. My life revolved around procedures and treatments for so long that I did not recognize the signs of my struggling mental status. I was working part-time while applying for jobs, but I was unsure of what I wanted to do professionally. I was unfamiliar with this version of myself. Fighting cancer was my full-time job for three years and did not notice I had won the war. I was unaware of what next steps looked like let alone how to begin them. I was unemployed emotionally and physically and lost mentally until I made peace with the fact that 2015 Neosho was no longer and that I needed to get to know 2019 Neosho.

Just when I began to understand myself, I realized I'd been struggling with ADHD. I knew it was time to be formally tested and begin therapy. I realized so many of my health issues, such as weight and high blood pressure, could be traced back to my attention deficiency. It is funny how regimented I was while going through cancer treatment. I mean, I love a good routine and when I didn't have a scheduled appointment or upcoming procedure, I was stuck. In addition to my issues with ADHD, I had begun feeling like I had PTSD due to all of the trauma I had endured during the previous three years.

During one visit, I tried to be open and transparent with Dr. Ahmed in hopes that she could help me.

"Dr. Ahmed, I have ADHD. Were it not for Adderall I would not have finished my dissertation," I said.

"Are you still taking Adderall?" she asked.

"No, ma'am. I took it until my doctor moved out of the area. The next doctor was not certified to prescribe it."

"Okay. Where were you tested for ADHD?" she asked.

"I wasn't formally tested. I shared my difficulty focusing while writing my dissertation and he recognized the symptoms and prescribed me ten milligrams of Adderall. It completely changed my writing," I said.

"Well, I can start you with five milligrams of Adderall, but I am going to refer you to the weight loss clinic. They have a therapist there who can prescribe those meds and determine if you need a permanent therapist," she explained.

As I shared my struggles with Dr. Ahmed, I realized I definitely needed therapy. She suggested I look at the residency clinic on campus for testing. Per the doctor's suggestion, I made an appointment with Dr. Singh in the weight loss clinic and registered with the Meltzer Center for formal testing.

I got the call to begin testing for ADHD the same week I began a new job as an executive assistant. I know you are wondering if I can be an executive assistant with ADHD and if you aren't, you should be. *What the heck was I thinking?* Then again, I was thinking I needed a job that paid enough to move into my own place. My contract with the part-time job ended so that full-time role came right on time. I was thankful I could make enough money to move on my own. That job was a gift and a curse. While it may not have been my *ministry*, I was not horrible at the job.

According to William Dodson, MD (2021) for people with ADHD, Rejection Sensitive Dysphoria (RSD) can mean extreme emotional sensitivity and pain triggered by the perception that someone important to them has been criticizing or rejecting them. RSD also may be triggered by falling short or failing to meeting their own high expectations. I realized I have been suffering from RSD my entire life! I was always a sensitive kid to the point of being taunted by my older family members for crying and taking things so personally. While they did not mean to inflict harm, I have found that due to RSD those experiences lingered. Those early experiences led to me putting up walls to block out the fear and pain that came with my sensitivity. The walls covered my crying and my vulnerabilities, which hid my true self from the world. It was a conversation with my best friend, John, that opened my pandora's box of fear of vulnerability.

So, just imagine me being told by someone I loved and respected that I had to leave my home while I was sick or jumping from room rental to room rental, while battling a severe burn and undergoing several surgeries or asking people about employment opportunities only to be ghosted time and time again. Fighting breast cancer without a husband or biological family nearby was extremely lonely, but coupled with the pain of rejection from friends and people I admired, was unbearable at times. But God . . .

God created some situations and allowed others to occur, but I trusted it was not for naught. I was scheduled to move on Saturday, February 15, but due to a water leak in the building, they had to replace the floor. So, I had to stay at my old place two weeks longer than I expected. And then, the craziest thing happened, I lost my job on Friday, February 28. I felt like Craig in the movie, *Friday*! I was fired on my day off! So, you know how Craig went in to get his check and then was fired? Well, I went in for what I thought was a quick meeting. I was not a perfect executive assistant, but I had done nothing to deserve being terminated after four months, especially when it takes at least nine months to a year to really get the hang of a job. Yes, I did some internal research. Thankfully, I kept my composure and received the message that it was time to move on. But the timing sucked! I had movers scheduled, boxes packed, and my deposit was paid that morning. I definitely yelled in my head, "Really, God? Really!"

Welp, at this point, I figured things could only get better. Uh... No! The next day, Saturday, February 29, I moved into my first place where I did not have roommates: a sunny, first floor condo that included off-street parking. I was beyond excited, until I arrived to find there was still no flooring, the same stained carpet in the bedroom, and an unclean bathroom. The emperor of irony strikes again! I was in shock with tears in my eyes. I mean I had nowhere to go, but my tears were quickly replaced by a chuckle, a smirk, and shaking head. I didn't think he would make it easy, but no floor? *C'mon man!* I thought I was being punk'd!

I figured I'd been through worse, plus I found the greatest comfort in gratitude. Despite losing my job the day before moving, I had enough funds to hold me over for a month or so and the real estate company was extremely apologetic and accommodating about the floor and cleaning. I was in my own home. Gratitude was an understatement. I prayed and thanked God repeatedly, all while sleeping in a cramped bedroom on an air mattress with all of my belongings stacked all around me. There was nowhere to put anything in the living area, but that was fine with me because I was comforted in knowing I was not worried about roommates coming into my living space without notice or afraid of the landlord abruptly evicting me. It was just me and Jesus!

After a week of eating out and living out of boxes with no floor, I was looking forward to celebrating my fortieth birthday with my Pink Sisters at the Young Survival Coalition's (YSC) Annual Summit in Los Angeles. YSC is an international organization that provides resources and community for young people affected by breast cancer. Well, the excitement was short lived, because the night before I was set to leave, the summit was canceled. The world was about to shut down due to the pending pandemic. Stubborn and hardheaded, I went to LA anyway expecting to hang out with friends for my fortieth, but the joke was on me. I was clueless to what was really going on since I did not have TV and internet at home. I didn't think it was that bad. Boy, was I wrong! I spent an awkward five days in Los Angeles, but enjoyed spending my birthday touring the Warner Bros lot and having dinner with the one person who wasn't sick or afraid to go out.

Returning to DC from LA was a hot mess! It was pouring rain my entire last day in LA and LAX airport looked like a ghost town. That was my first glimpse of what was to come. When I arrived back to Maryland, it was pouring rain. While driving home, I felt such a sense of peace. I was looking forward to meeting with my plastic surgeon the next day about a possible final surgery to even out my boobs. I was also excited to just sleep in my own space. Next thing I heard was a weird rubbing sound while driving. Of course, I have a flat due to the big-ass hook sticking out if my tire. *You have got to be kidding me!*

It was Friday, March 13, 1:30 am. While writing this book, I began to reflect on that date and time and realized that while my car was sitting in the pouring rain on a flat, Breonna Taylor's family were not aware that she had been murdered an hour before in her home and the world was about to lockdown due to the COVID-19 pandemic, forcing people to stay home. While all of this was occurring, I was just trying to make it home from a long trip. I was sitting in the middle of the night thinking of the saying, "when it rains, it pours." In this case, literally and figuratively.

When I finally made it home, I overslept and missed my doctor's appointment. By the time I woke up, people were stocking up on toilet paper and the world was shutting down one country at a time. Many people were freaking out, but it was easy to maintain a sense of normalcy since my world has been shut down before. By the end of the summer, I realized that losing my job could not come at a more perfect time. I do not think I could have worked that job during a pandemic. That was nothing but God removing me from a situation that would have made my life more difficult in the pandemic. The pandemic affected us all, but in a strange way, my crazy breast cancer journey prepared me for 2020. And God knew what I needed to get through it.

Breast cancer was a type of alchemy for me. Each person, location, treatment, and surgery provided some sort of transformation, thus changing the world around me. My sense of purpose and understanding of self was not what I thought. Through all of those hardships, I realized home is a conceptual dichotomy, between myself and shelter. I had a real estate situation which forced me to hit the reset button on being physically sheltered. I went from expecting home to be a place where I felt welcomed and comforted to a place of shelter. It took ten hours of ADHD testing and a pandemic to bring me home mentally and physically. I now know that every person I encountered throughout my cancer journey were all instruments with specific purposes. When the dust settles, I know where my help cometh from and who was sent for that purpose. While the pandemic forced most people to reevaluate their own understanding of home, my breast cancer journey had already changed my world to a point that I had to learn about myself in order to discover where home is.

After being formally tested for ADHD, I realized that living with roommates was not the best arrangement for me. I learned what home means to me, especially since my condition seemed to conflict with the lifestyle of others. I could not afford to settle for just anything. Living in discomfort could cause mental, spiritual, and physical harm. My Aunt Anita was adamant about me leaving my basement apartment because she believed the fear and anxiety of living in that toxic environment could lead to further health complications. This was proven while living with Ms. Jackie with an open wound in my chest in the June heat thus causing me to develop a severe infection. I am not saying my discomfort or pain was intentional, but the result of living in places that were uncomfortable caused mental and physical issues.

At the end of the movie, *The Wiz*, Dorothy, played by Diana Ross, sings a song called "Home." In the song, she describes home as a place with love overflowing and she speaks directly to God, begging him not to make it hard to believe what we see, then she asks if he could tell us if we should run away or if we should stay and let things be. When I began this journey, I did not know what home was to me. I thought it was where you felt comfortable, but what happens when that home is no longer comfortable. After living from house to house in search of stability and the comforts of home, I have evolved in my understanding of what home is within myself. I have had a few laughs at myself that I'm sure God orchestrated, including looking at places to live in the woods with hardly any cell service. *What the heck was I thinking?* I have not lived in my own place since leaving

Kansas City in 2005 and desperately wanted to live in a place similar to the basement apartment with my former landlord. God told me to move forward. I had to, as the gospel song goes, "Let Go and Let God" (Woods, 2006). After living in my own place for more than a year, I can't help but exclaim, "There's no place like home!"

But where do I go from here?

CHAPTER 17

THE BEST IS YET TO COME

———

As I reflect on my war with cancer, I think about all the battles I won and the people I lost. I do not believe that I lost a battle with cancer because I don't believe God makes mistakes. However, all of the people I lost be it to death, miscommunication, or just growth, still saddens me. The years following my diagnosis included an amusement park of rollercoaster rides, a few comedy specials of dark humor, and a song full of irony.

In addition to all you have read, my cancer journey has been blessings on blessings on blessings. I still think of what God meant when he said, "This is why you can't find a job. I have a bigger job for you." I still am not sure what that job is, but for now, I will continue to just live. I have recently struggled with survivor's guilt. The loss of fellow Howard Bison, Chadwick Boseman, was triggering. Since my diagnosis, I have gotten extremely sad whenever I learn of someone's cancer diagnosis, whether I knew them personally or not.

I now know what it was: survivor's guilt. I have to be great going forward because cancer has taken so many great people and I am still here. I have no choice. Plus, I am tired of being the punchline in God's jokes due to not listening or my impulsive decisions!

Occasionally, I've asked God, "Why me?"

He would immediately quip, "Why not you, daughter?"

While living with my radiation burn, I heard a sermon about God's most faithful servant, Job (pronounced JŌB). As the minister preached about Satan taking everything from Job, all I could think about is how cancer had taken so much from me. Then, the preacher reminded us that it was Job's faith that prompted God to suggest for Satan to consider him in the first place. *You missed your shout* Satan took everything from Job and inflicted bodily harm on him, but per God's instructions, Satan could not take Job's life. Job endured unimaginable pain and suffering, but he remained faithful to God. Despite the sins of his wife and children, Job's faith never wavered and in return, he was blessed. I do not pretend to be perfect, but I saw so much of myself in that sermon! I said, "In a twenty-first century way, I am Job." I endured so much bodily harm due to my cancer treatments and surgery, but through it all my faith remained.

The flesh is weak and I came up against some hardships that shook me to my core, but the answers were tattooed on my wrist the whole time, Proverbs 3:5-6. "Trust in the Lord with all your heart and lean not on your own understanding; In all ways acknowledge him, and he will direct your paths."

As I ran into life's roadblocks, I would feel God's laughter which in turn would make me laugh. His jokes were more humorous than laugh out loud funny. I found them to be chalked full of *a-ha* moments and tough love. I realized my laughter was a form of therapy, and I needed to be humbled. I learned the importance of vulnerability and recognized my struggles with it. He knew that this journey would eventually be shared, thus exposing me for who I am and *whose* I am. Just like God has an interesting sense of humor, so do I. So, I get it. We all have a personal relationship with God, so I am not telling you what to laugh at. I am only sharing how I overcame so much by seeing God's humor through it all. God knows that I would not lie or fabricate my story to gain notoriety or for money. He created me to give it to you straight, no chaser, and I am being obedient. The journey continues.

The biggest hurdle I can't seem to clear is a successful, impactful career, which was a challenge before cancer. Go figure! I laugh at how I have received so many job rejections over the past year. These are jobs I know I am qualified for, and in some cases overqualified for, and yet I don't make it past the initial interview. On one hand, I could be a poor interviewer, but the way these conversations go, I was left shocked when I didn't hear back. It is at those times when I am reminded that sometimes it is not about my qualifications, level of education, or connections. It is at those times when I am reminded of God's comedic timing. When I look back over the past five years, all I can say is, "God's Got Jokes!"

I always acknowledged His presence and hand in all of my trials and triumphs. When you are humbled by a chronic illness such as cancer, you have no choice but to lean on Him. I noticed that in the hardships I endured, from homelessness to surgical complications, I found God's humor in it all. My help and healing came from that humor, which in turn, strengthened my faith. I also came to recognize the angels God sent to my aid. The more transparent and vulnerable I was, the more people saw I needed assistance. Opening up like that took its toll, but I was afraid to show it. How to you share your previous thoughts of suicide with friends who could recommend you for a job? After a while, I was even reluctant to tell people when I was in pain for fear that it would be used against me in some way.

Let's stop sugar coating our mental and physical health. These are topics that will naturally cause discomfort, but I believe in taking those topics to God in prayer. I am not saying don't be afraid or uncomfortable because we are human, but when you approach life's biggest obstacles with fear and worry, it cancels out faith and prayer. Don't get me wrong, I am not saying to only pray; I believe in therapy, but it has to be grounded in faith. I am a witness that faith without works is dead.

Like I tell people all the time, tell me the truth no matter what. I will cry in the car. We all shy away from life's hard truths because it exposes our vulnerabilities. So, the way I see it, it is not about whether you will laugh at my truths. It is about me getting these testimonies off my eight-times reconstructed chest, feel me? Sharing this journey is my truth and I pray it helps someone discover theirs. None of us are alone in this thing called life. We all have shit! I am thankful I refused to suffer in silence. I am grateful for the journey as a whole because I know I was not on it alone, despite my loneliness. My ancestors, family, and friends were with me along the way, but God made sure

His presence was known. The setbacks I experienced could have taken me out, but God had other plans. What do I do with this beautiful struggle? What is the bigger job God has for me? In my moments of loneliness, I am reminded of why he kept me.

We are all familiar with Deuteronomy 31:8 that says, "He will never leave you nor forsake you." Well, what some may have missed in that part of scripture is that Moses says that phrase twice. Once to the people he led out of bondage and then again directly to Joshua, who God chose to lead His people into the Promised Land. Moses reiterated this phrase directly to Joshua after telling him to be strong and courageous. Even after Joshua heard Moses tell the people the Lord will not leave them nor forsake them, Moses knew Joshua needed to hear that for himself. When you are about to embark on a life-changing journey, it can seem overwhelming and debilitating. What separates believers from non-believers is that believers know they are not alone, thus making them fearless and undeterred. That was me on this cancer journey undeterred.

Now, I believed he would never leave me nor forsake me, but I can also hear God saying, "Since, I'm here, I may as well tell a few jokes along the way," which translates as, "I won't leave you nor forsake you, but since you are hard-headed and stubborn, you gon' get these jokes!" After a good cry, I could feel the comfort of laughter. The beauty in my struggle is that with the pain came the humor.

I still have so much I hope to accomplish in this second act. When I feel doubt or disappointment, I look at my wrist. In addition to acknowledging him, I am finding strength in my vulnerability. I am exactly where God wants me to be:

broke and looking for a job, but healthy and happy. I never have to ask who's got jokes, because God always does and I love it! This is just the end of *this* book, but like the book of Genesis, there are more books that follow. I have it on good authority that the best is yet to come!

ACKNOWLEDGMENTS

First and foremost, THANK YOU, JESUSSSSS!! This book would not have been possible without the Father, the Son, and the Holy Spirit.

Thank you to all three sides of my family, Ponder, Maltbia/Jacks, and McGee/Lang for my foundation that is grounded in faith, family, love, and humor. I would not be ME without you!

My best friend, confidant, voice of reason, Gabriel's dad and Josh's husband, "Felipé José", I could have gotten through any of this without your unwavering support. I am so glad I sat behind you in Spanish class almost 30 years ago. We have literally been through life and death. Thank you for being my friend!

Thank you to my devastating and dynamic Sorors of Delta Sigma Theta Sorority, Inc. for 22 years of the unbreakable bond of sisterhood, especially my line sisters, Tiffany, Tionna, and Kay. I'm not an Ace without you!

I am blessed to be a member of the greatest church on this side of glory, Reid Temple AME Church! The prayers, meals, rent payments, hospital visits and rides, moving help, and agape love saved my life. Thank you, Pastor Washington and

Pastor Whitlock, for your leadership and teachings throughout my cancer and book journeys!

To my Pink Sisters, Unicorn Squad, Sisterhood of 'AutHERS', Sista-Friends, and Homies, your encouragement and support have been immeasurable, from late night co-working zooms to helping me overcome moments of doubt and writers block, you have all made a significant difference in my life and could not have completed this book without you!

Shout-out to my Campaign Village who believed in my story enough to help me bring "God's Got Jokes" to the world:

Aaron Gatlin
Alexandria Harris
Acasia Olson
Alexis Corbitt
Adrian Richards
Amy Knieriem
Aida Fitzgerald
Andres Marquez-Lara
Allyson Criner Brown
Anita Williams
Allyson Hernandez
April Finley
Anjuan Durant
Ashley Ward
Chalet Hannah
Aunt Anita Maltbia
Charles Miller
Blondy Moore
Craig Hughes

Carleen Lynn
  Burke-Fernandes
Cranston Gittens
Carolyn McCornac
Crecilla Cohen Scott
Chanelle Hardy
Darrian Witt
Christlena Lockhart
Davon Bagley
Christopher Martino
Dele Lowman Smith
Christopher Wade
Desiree Lee
Dan Washington
Dorothy Myers
Denise Cook
Dr. Michelle Hubert-Pegram
Donna Barnes
Dr. Regina Warren
Dr. Barbara Hines

Dr. Sharon Byrd
Dr. Joe Seabrooks
Dr. Tariqah Nuriddin
Dr. Peggy Lewis
Dr. Tia Tyree
Dr. Tekisha Everette
Elizabeth Ljung
Dy Brown
Beth Napper
Edina Robinson
Gabrielle Cantave
Erika Stevenson
Jacqueline Alexander
Hadith Zalzala
Jamica Davis
Ingrid Sturgis
Jasmin Nelson
Jacquelyn Edmiston
Jeannie Williams
Jemellia Hilfiger
Jenee Bagby
Jennifer Bowman
Joey Thomas
Karen Mitchell
Kameelah Dixon
Katherine Fritzsche
Karen Turner
Kay Young
Keela Seales
Ken Lumpkins
Kenya Cassell
Kimberly Jones

Kenya Stevens
Kristin Clarkson
Kezia Williams
Laurie Rowe
Kim Terry
Louise Waller
Kristin DiBiase
Luba Chaffee
Kristin Wiley
Marlana Dickerson
Krysten Thomas
Mary Franklin
LaDavia Drane
Maurice Lang Jr.
LaKesha Bunn
Min. Eva Clark
Laverne Parks
Nikia Maltbia
Le'Kedra Robertson
Nina Sharon Carter
Lea Douglin Brown
Pamela O'Leary
Lesley Kilp
Patricia Page
Marjorie Innocent
Regina Wagner
Marquita Sanders
Rev. Donna Barnes
Mysiki Valentine
Rob Byrd
Nefertara Clark
Rosalind Cochran

Nicole Battle
Sean Conner
Nina Smith
Seneca Brown
Phillip Santoli
Shauntel Ellis
Randall Logan
Shelia Atkinson
ReGina Davis
Stacey Jacks
René Brooks
Starr Barbour
Rev. Chania Dillard
Ten Grant
Rev. LaTisha Thomas
  Cokely
Teneille Walker

Rev. Reggie White
Terrance Goldston
Sandida Moss
Tiffany Hamilton
Schcola Chambers
Tina Lacey
Stephen Long
Tyra Banks
Tausha Brooks
Warnelia Page
Tionna Wilson
William Thomas
Tracy Worley
Yvonne Francis
Veronica Becton
Zelda Davis
Will Wilder

APPENDIX

CHAPTER 1

Maltby, Anna. "The New ADHD Debate Every Woman Should Know About," *O Magazine,* November 2014. https://www.oprah.com/health/adult-adhd-diagnosis-adhd-medication.

CHAPTER 3

Songfacts. "When Doves Cry – Songfacts" 2021. https://www.songfacts.com/facts/prince/when-doves-cry.

CHAPTER 5

Gibson, Brian, dir. *What's Love Got to Do With It.* 1993; Los Angeles, CA: Touchstone Pictures. Videocassette (VHS), 118 min.

CHAPTER 8

Beastie Boys, *License to Ill,* Def Jam Recordings/Columbia Records, 1986, vinyl LP.

Fieg, Paul, dir. *Bridesmaids.* 2011; Los Angeles, CA: Universal Pictures, DVD.

CHAPTER 9

Hammond, Fred and Radical for Christ, *The Spirit of David*, Benson – 84418-4320-2, 1996, compact disc.

MaeTV. "In Living Color Season 2 Episode 14." March 20, 2013. Video, 23:10. https://www.youtube.com/watch?v=Ewy1L-1Ha8O4

CHAPTER 10

BrainyQuote. *Walter Winchell - A Real Friend is One Who Walks in When the Rest of the World Walks Out*, 2021. https://www.brainyquote.com/quotes/walter_winchell_121442.

Brown, Tabitha (@IamTabithaBrown). "Donna is having a little deep conditioning and @donnasrecipe pamper session so she and I are making up and I think we gonna be on good terms this week We thank y'all for the prayers because she done came back with a good word. When it/they shed naturally let it go!" *Instagram*, video 2:57, October 24, 2021. https://www.instagram.com/tv/CVbxPvSsAnF/?utm_medium=copy_link.

CHAPTER 11

Arie, India. *Testimony, Volume 1: Life & Relationships,* Motown Records, 2006, compact disc.

CHAPTER 12

Ponder, Neosho. "This is 37... #Forward *Warning: Graphic Pics Again*." *CaringBridge – Neosho Ponder Journal* (blog). March 20, 2017. https://www.caringbridge.org/visit/neoshoponder/journal.

CHAPTER 13

BreastCancer.org. *DIEP Flap.* Last modified March 7, 2019. https://www.breastcancer.org/treatment/surgery/reconstruction/types/autologous/diep

Ponder, Neosho. "Happy Holidays (Wish I had Better News)." *CaringBridge – Neosho Ponder Journal* (blog). December 31, 2017. https://www.caringbridge.org/visit/neoshoponder/journal.

CHAPTER 14

Heidekrueger, Paul I., Nicholas Moellhoff, Raymund E. Horch, Jörn A. Lohmeyer, Mario Marx, Christoph Heitmann, Hisham Fansa, Matthias Geenen, Christian J. Gabka, Steffen Handstein, Lukas Prantl, and Uwe von Fritschen. "Overall Complication Rates of DIEP Flap Breast Reconstructions in Germany—A Multi-Center Analysis Based on the DGPRÄC Prospective National Online Registry for Microsurgical Breast Reconstructions" Journal of Clinical Medicine 10, no. 5 (2021): 1016. https://doi.org/10.3390/jcm10051016.

Ponder, Neosho. "What Were You Doing 2 Years Ago, Today, August 23, 2016." *CaringBridge – Neosho Ponder Journal* (blog). August 23, 2018. https://www.caringbridge.org/visit/neoshoponder/journal.

CHAPTER 17

Dodson, MD, William. "How ADHD Ignites Rejection Sensitive Dysphoria". *Attitude.* Updated August 24, 2021. https://www.additudemag.com/rejection-sensitive-dysphoria-and-adhd/.

Lumet, Sidney, dir. *The Wiz.* 1978; Queens, NY: NBC Universal, April 20, 2011. YouTube Movies.

Woods, DeWayne. *Introducing DeWayne Woods & When Singers Meet.* Verity – 85333-2, 2006, compact disc.